PAULA MILNE was born in Buck̲ ̲g̲ ̲ ̲ ̲ ̲ ̲ ̲ ̲ in 19 ̲ ̲.
She studied Fine Art at the Central School of Art and
Design, and subsequently took a postgraduate course in
film-making at the Royal College of Art. In 1973 she joined
the BBC as a script editor, where she devised the original
series *Angels*. In 1976 she left the BBC to become a
freelance writer. She has innumerable television credits,
including contributions to *Z-Cars, Coronation Street,
Angels, Juliet Bravo, Crown Court,* and many others. She
was responsible for dramatising *My Father's House* and
The Sidmouth Letters, and more recently, she has written a
four-part *Love Story* for the BBC, two 'Plays for Today' and
a six-part series aimed at teenage girls. She is regarded as
one of the most promising young television writers in
Britain today. This is Paula Milne's first novel. She lives in
London with her husband and three young children, and is
at present working on her second novel.

Utterly surprising and often funny, *John David* is about
people facing the unfaceable, and how they do it. It is the
story of a birth and its aftermath, of an emotional and moral
dilemma now immensely topical. For John David is born
mentally handicapped, with Down's syndrome, and Judith,
his mother, decides she will not keep her child. The bitter
consequences of this decision bring to the surface unac-
knowledged conflicts, not only within Judith herself, but in
her marriage and her family relationships. Paula Milne's
confrontation with the shattering emotions parents feel at
the birth of a mongol child is based on her own experiences.
This is a remarkably honest, disquieting novel, and an
intensely moving one.

JOHN DAVID

Paula Milne

Virago

For Peter, for bearing
no resemblance to Patrick

Published by VIRAGO PRESS Limited 1982
Ely House, 37 Dover Street, London W1X 4HS

Copyright © Paula Milne 1982

Typeset by Coats Dataprint Ltd.
and printed by the Anchor Press,
of Tiptree, Essex

British Library Cataloguing in Publication Data
Milne, Paula
John David.
I. Title
823'.914[F]   PR6063.I378/

ISBN 0-86068-236-6
ISBN 0-86068-237-4 Pbk

Chapter One

The afternoon before the baby was born, Judith's mother called round. As usual, she did not announce her arrival, but simply walked around the side of the house and through the back door which led directly into the sitting room. Judith was lying on the sofa, watching a court-room drama on a portable black and white television. The room for once was in disarray, but Judith's mother was at ease with disarray and chaos. She had an antipathy towards polished surfaces and dust-free cornices. A clean oven, she had once been heard to remark, was the sign of an empty mind. She was given to such utterances. Judith's mother was an artist. However, her much-quoted artistic temperament rarely manifested itself in any coherent creative form. Rather it was demonstrated in her unorthodox dress, in the perpetual arc of dirt encrusted under her finger-nails (from gardening, she said, though her garden was a neglected jungle of brambles). Then there were her views, as inconsistent as they were unpredictable, which she could defend with a tenacity which was disconcerting.

She stood now, in the middle of the sitting room, her threadbare duffel coat hanging thickly about her, her hair spilling in a ragged grey cascade over the hood. She had an angular face, the skin only barely wrinkled, pulled tautly over the protruding cheekbones and the sharp peninsular of her jaw. Holding a bulging launderette bag, looking neither at her daughter nor commenting on the uncharacteristic untidiness of the room, she gazed instead at the television, momentarily arrested by the image of the man in the dock. 'You're getting obese,' she remarked. 'You should cut out the carbohydrates. You're blowing up like a barrage balloon.'

'I know.'

Judith was undismayed by her mother's bluntness, she had spent twenty years growing up with it and a further five growing away from it. Her fingers moved involuntarily to her abdomen where she felt the baby shudder tremulously within her. It was a habit she had developed at some moments, (withdrawal tactics, Patrick called it), and the baby always rose magnificently to the occasion, mutely responding to her kneading fingers, fluttering its reply like morse code. At such times they were in league, she drawing nourishment and solace from the baby as it in turn drew nourishment and succour from her. And she had created it! Little Judith who had wept over the placing of decimal points and sewed her own name tapes on her school uniform. Judith with her perpetual weight problem and her stubbornly average I.Q. Judith – whose unremarkable childhood was to be remembered only by a few faded photographs and a collection of pencil marks charting her growth rate etched on to her mother's kitchen wall. Judith the obscure and obscured was at last to triumph. She was with child. Beyond that goal, now so nearly attained, she had no aspiration.

✳   ✳   ✳

'What have you got there?' she asked, and her mother, on cue, dropped the launderette bag on to a chair and pulled from it items of baby clothes: a jacket, a shawl, several cot blankets, limp and discoloured from washing, collected no doubt from bring-and-buy sales and well-meaning neighbours. Judith enthused dutifully. Such gestures were rare for her mother and she knew better than to discourage them. Later she made tea. Her mother sat in the kitchen, one trousered thigh crossed over its companion, cigarette in hand, talking of her own confinement; how Judith had thrust and torn her way into the world, feet first, as her mother cursed the white-faced nurses attending her.

Chapter One

It was an anecdote Judith had heard before. She stood listening, wiping the surfaces of her kitchen, occasionally intercepting with a sympathetic word, but refusing to identify her mother's experience with the imminence of her own.

✳   ✳   ✳

At half past six Patrick returned home from work. Since Cynthia showed no signs of departing he tactfully offered her a gin and tonic and they withdrew to the sitting room, where Cynthia started talking about visiting times at the hospital.

'I've got them all written down if you want them,' Judith said, as she lowered herself into an armchair, 'although the first visit is restricted to husbands only.'

'As it happens, I'm going in on my own account.'

Judith looked at her mother sharply.

'What's the matter with you?'

'Does something have to be the matter with me? I'm simply having a check-up.'

'People don't go into hospital for no reason, Mother.'

'Nonsense, they do it all the time.'

Cynthia swallowed the remainder of her gin and held out her glass to Patrick for a refill.

'I'm forty-eight years old and it's time I was checked over.'

'We might even be in hospital on the same day, you never know.' She smiled benignly at her recumbent daughter. 'I'll be able to pop down and witness the great event.'

Judith made no comment; instead she turned to Patrick, suggesting that the thermostat on the central heating be turned up. The room seemed suddenly cold.

✳   ✳   ✳

That night Judith stood naked in front of the dressing-table mirror in the bedroom, listening to the familiar sound of Patrick locking up the house beneath her, covertly contemplating her body. Her abdomen hung ponderously before her, its cantilevered underbelly criss-crossed by a lattice-work of purple stretch marks. She turned sideways and, as she did, the baby lurched alarmingly within her. For a second her whole abdomen seemed to twist and distort under its impact. A moment later she felt a heavy ache throb deep inside her. The head had engaged, she knew it with complete certainty. A thrill of excitement charged through her. It no longer struck her, as it had previously done on these nightly reveries in front of the mirror, that this ungainly protruberance, with its dark and liquid interior, was the home of her unborn child. It seemed to her now like a cage, trapping the reluctant baby within it.

Chapter Two

The pains were coming at half-hourly intervals, accompanied by a low, gnawing back-ache, just as the book described. Patrick held her wrist while she started on her breathing exercises. An hour later he made tea, and they sat drinking it in bed, monitoring her contractions. They agreed they would phone the hospital only when labour was properly established and an hour later there was no doubt that it was. While Judith lay in bed, propped up by pillows, panting and blowing her way through each rising contraction, Patrick found his car keys and the hospital telephone number.

They had agreed, too, to be open-minded about his

presence at the birth – that he must feel no guilt if he felt he couldn't cope with the trauma of it all. It was important, they felt, to know one's limitations in these situations. However Patrick had secretly acquired several Valium tablets from a colleague at work: he had kept them wrapped in tin foil in his breast pocket, and he now unwrapped them and hastily swallowed one in the bathroom.

Another hour passed. The pain of the contractions was intensifying. Judith experienced a stab of panic as her body took possession of her. Momentarily she forgot her breathing as a heaving contraction tightened, vice-like, around her belly. Stars shot in front of her eyes, her thoughts became disconnected; her back arched and her fingers clawed at the air. The image of Patrick swam briefly into her vision, standing transfixed and wide-eyed as she writhed and struggled on the bed before him. The room seemed suddenly hot, the bed damp beneath her. She could feel the baby, crouched like a coiled spring inside her. The pain swept upwards, like the crest of a wave, bearing her ahead of it in an agony so intense that she felt that part of her mind which was still intact and unviolated rise up in angry revolt. They never said it would be like this, those cashmere women at the natural childbirth classes with their Paisley cushions and sensible shoes. They had betrayed her with their cheerful stoicism and well chosen euphemisms about the stages of labour. This was not something that could be quantified with diagrams or neatly separated into stages, numbering one to three. This was pain, and she was disintegrating under it.

*   *   *

They drove to the hospital in silence, Judith concentrating on her contractions. She regarded them now as an enemy, waiting to invade her when she was unsuspecting and unprepared. But she would be prepared. She would outwit and outflank them. They were coming in five-minute intervals, each contraction was signalled in the same manner, a slow hot flush of discomfort spreading through her back and groin, which in turn signalled Judith to start her breathing, eyes fixed on some point on the car dashboard, huffing and puffing in and out, as her distended diaphragm struggled to keep pace with her. Patrick sat beside her silently, waiting for the traffic lights to change and the Valium to take effect.

As they swung into the hospital forecourt another thought seized Judith. The memory of her mother's recent words about her own, as yet unexplained, admission to the hospital returned, and the horrific image of Cynthia in the labour room, watching her agony and inadequacy became somehow confused with the pain itself, which was threatening to engulf her once more. She closed her eyes and took a deep breath but became aware of a voice urgently calling out. It was Patrick.

'Dear God . . . don't start pushing here. Not now.'

* * *

She felt calmer once they were inside the hospital. The bright lights and gleaming instruments instantly relaxed her. They were met at the entrance by a harassed nurse with cropped hair and muscular legs. She led them into a small, white-washed room where she took Judith's pulse while Patrick hovered uncertainly over them. The nurse noted Judith's attempts at her breathing with practised approval.

'That's the idea, love. Keep that up and you'll do just fine.'

She spoke like someone middle-aged but in reality she was only a year or so older than Judith herself. The uniform lent her an ageless, tireless efficiency. She turned now to Patrick, with a perfunctory indulgent smile.

Chapter Two

'I suggest you trot off and get yourself a hot drink while I get your wife ready. There's a machine up the corridor. All right?'

She framed it as a question but it had an authority about it, and Patrick was quick to obey. Gratefully he pecked Judith's cheek, squeezed her arm reassuringly, and was gone.

Without Patrick's presence the nurse's manner softened. She asked Judith her Christian name, and told her to lie on the bed while she continued her examination. Blood pressure and temperature were taken and meticulously recorded. The contractions were more frequent now and, as Judith braced herself for them, the nurse rested a cool hand on her straining abdomen. They waited together in companionable silence.

'It's your first, then?' the nurse remarked eventually.

Judith nodded mutely, conserving her energies for the battle raging within her. The nurse smiled encouragingly, her hand on the heaving belly fluttering in a professional gesture of sympathy. A moment passed, the pain was there again, Judith rolled about on the narrow bed, grunting back her screams, feeling the baby thrust remorselessly on its downward path to freedom. Between the contractions she would slump feebly back, incredulous that she could not remember the pain of the last contraction nor visualise the one that lay ahead. It seemed that her mind as well as her body was determined to betray her. She drank in each second of the brief respite from pain as if it were to be her last.

The nurse was doing things to her again. Hands encased in clammy polythene gloves were plunged inside her. More notes were entered on the chart. Another nurse, painfully young with an anxious, furrowed brow, briefly made an appearance and left again. Enema pellets were inserted; she was led to a lavatory where she sat shivering, waiting for her bowels to obey and they did so.

7

How could they not? Back on the narrow bed her legs were parted and a razor chewed noisily at her pubic hair. She closed her eyes. Outside she could hear a telephone ring, footsteps running down the corridor. Then silence. The nurse now sat beside her, one hand still propped proprietorially on her abdomen, clipboard of charts on her lap, pen and fob watch at the ready. Judith waited for a contraction to pass before turning to her.

'When do I get my epidural?'

The nurse blinked at her.

'My dear, you're two thirds dilated.'

The words had some vague significance and Judith struggled to remember their meaning. Something about the lip of the cervix she recalled; in her pregnancy manual there had been a diagram of a sphere with one outer edge chopped off. Was that the lip? She frowned in concentration.

'All the same, I think I'll have one,' she said eventually, in a tone which she hoped would brook no argument.

The dire warnings of friends now returned to her, about over-zealous doctors and nurses and the need to be unequivocal in one's demands lest they should be ignored. The nurse pursed her lips in calculated patience.

'There's no time. Your cervix is well on the way to being fully dilated. If you wanted one you should have said something before.'

She spoke disapprovingly. Judith felt childlike under the rebuke, as was the intention. Tears stung the back of her eyes. True, she had practised her breathing to perfection, but she always had the consoling knowledge that an epidural would be there if she needed it. But now it was to be denied to her, apparently through her own fault. Desolation swamped her. This was not how she had planned it at all. In a petulant voice she demanded that her husband be returned to her. When he was ushered in she heard herself wailing that she wasn't to be allowed her epidural. He shifted his weight uncomfortably, replying that the nurses probably knew best.

Half an hour later she was wheeled into the labour room. A transparent plastic babies' basinette stood in readiness by the bed. She stared at it uncomprehendingly. In the anguish of her pain she had forgotten that it was all in aid of a baby, but somehow the thought didn't comfort her as it should have done.

The room filled with people. Patrick, gowned and masked, sat beside her, a hand grimly gripping hers. A masked doctor and midwife exchanged cheerful pleasant-ries as they scrubbed up in a corner. Three saucer-like discs of metal were clamped to her shuddering abdomen, then she could see the contractions etched, like sentinels, on to graph paper which spewed silently out of a machine by the bed. In the diminishing pauses between the contractions the sight of it brought a vague relief. At those moments, unable to recall the pain so recently experienced or anticipate the one to come, she almost believed she was imagining the whole thing. But those spidery lines affirmed its existence, providing a visible testament of her ordeal; her pain would not go entirely unremembered or unrecorded. Then, all at once, she was overwhelmed by the desire to push. It gripped her with an urgency which made the previous pains seem meagre by comparison. She was dimly aware of Patrick's hesitant presence on one side of her, and on the other the nurse who had admitted her baldly shouting instructions. The voice of the nurse became her life-line. The pain, unimaginable in its ferocity, was enveloping her; only that brusque commanding voice could splice through it. A vision of the room flashed briefly before her. A mask descended over her face.

'Push, Judith!' The voice of the nurse barked out at her

as if from nowhere. 'Push! Not like that, down towards your pelvis!'

Obediently, she heaved and groaned and pushed. A ragged chorus of instructions screamed at her again.

'PUSH!'

'Harder, come on!'

'One more for luck – you can do it!'

'Its head keeps disappearing on me!'

The pain changed from black to blood red.

'PUSH!'

'Again – come on!'

'Push, girl – that's it!'

Now she could feel the baby's head herself, plunging and rocking between her spreadeagled legs. Her feet were hoisted up in stirrups, one hand gripped by Patrick, the other by the nurse. She felt she was being crucified.

'PUSH!'

'Don't give in now – !'

'Only one more – come *on*!'

'Push!'

Still the baby lumpenly lurched back and forth within her.

'PUSH!'

The tones of the voices had altered. She recognised a note of alarm which had not been present before. Patrick's hand released hers, to be replaced by another, cold and inert.

'PUSH!'

A second machine was pushed up next to the first.

'We're just going to attach an electrode to the baby's head, love. Make sure its heart is functioning okay.'

The room shimmered and shifted in front of her, in synchrony, it seemed, with the baby thrusting and plunging within her.

'PUSH!'

The mask descended briefly again. Blackness.

10

Chapter Two

'PUSH!'

The mask was whisked away. She opened her eyes. The new machine was uttering agitated, irregular, high-pitched bleeps.

'PUSH!'

A gown rustled by her face. The bleeps faltered and fell silent. Now the doctors' voices cracked out.

'We'd better get this show on the road!'

'PUSH!'

She ached and strained in compliance. Her legs shook uncontrollably. Her back felt sore and bruised. Dismally she laboured on.

'PUSH!'

Their voices swelled in a crescendo somewhere above her. She braced herself for one last heave, one last attempt to get the wretched child born.

'PUSH!'

Another voice joined the others. She recognised it instantly, shamefully, as her own.

'Mother!' it yelled beseechingly, as the red blanket of pain descended. 'Mother!'

It was over. The baby slithered out, damp and cold between her legs. A cry of triumph rippled round the room. The door opened, Patrick reappeared, goggle-eyed above his mask.

'It's a boy,' someone said and her heart sank. The green gowns converged, collecting around the baby. A wet sponge was hastily applied to her forehead. Her legs were still strapped to the stirrups; she lay, gaping and forgotten. She caught a snatched glimpse of the infant, bloodied and dangling in gloved hands, its genitals drooping drearily beneath it.

She closed her eyes. All this for a boy.

Chapter Three

Judith had virtually no memory of her father. He and Cynthia were divorced before her second birthday. Although he had private misgivings about Cynthia's aptitude as a mother, he did not question her custodial rights over Judith, indeed she did not give him the opportunity. She did however give him the right to visit Judith, but it seemed the child only had eyes for her mother, and after a few months his visits stopped. Cynthia did not talk about him again, and Judith did not ask. He was absent, even in their silence.

As a child, Judith would look at her friends' mothers and marvel. They would offer her madeira cake in immaculate sitting rooms and sit in crisp crimplene rows at school concerts. Of her friends' fathers she would later recall little, but the memory of those ranks of meticulous mothers never left her. It was not that Cynthia had failed to provide affection, it was simply that she had difficulty in demonstrating it.

Neither did Cynthia fail to provide food and a home. Judith didn't go hungry and wasn't their home, although shabby and neglected, one of the biggest in the neighbourhood? No, Cynthia's failure was more subtle and pervasive than any of these. She simply failed to provide her young daughter with any continuity or routine. An innocuous enough omission to some, but Judith was a conventional child, perhaps made the more so by her mother's excesses.

Then there were the different men who sporadically trouped through their lives, leaving cigar butts floating in the lavatory and their cars parked in the double garage. There would be noisy, argumentative dinner parties; and impromptu holidays abroad, which Judith usually spent incarcerated in some hotel room listening to the World

Service while her mother sat in the darkened bowels of the hotel bar with her companion of the moment.

Money, or the lack of it, was a problem too. It did not noticeably inhibit Cynthia's mood or life-style until the envelopes containing the bank statement would flop through the letter box. There would follow days of teutonic silence and chain-smoking while Cynthia morosely thumbed through her cheque stubs, occasionally hugging Judith in a breathy, nicotine embrace, asking forgiveness for mismanaging their lives so. And Judith always forgave. If there was continuity in her life, it was that.

* * *

Judith had been in her second year at Sheffield University when she met Patrick. He was studying engineering and she geography. They frequented the same reference library, and after weeks of acknowledging each other with only a nod, the relationship developed. He did not seem actively to seek her out, yet she had only to turn her head and there he would be, outside a lecture theatre or crossing the campus towards her, the same words of casual greeting on his lips. So the pattern of her self-styled solitary existence imperceptibly shifted to one of shared companionship. She accepted Patrick's absent attentions and, consciously or not, found herself increasingly depending on them.

Sex took the same pattern. Passion, sexual or otherwise, was foreign to Patrick's nature. He shared a modest flat with two other engineering students, and on Friday nights, while they were out, he and Judith would make love, unhurriedly but efficiently, on the sofa. Afterwards she would cook them spaghetti bolognese on his Baby Belling and he would walk her home. It was a ritual which rarely varied.

She began to see that Patrick's lassitude had a certainty

about it, an uncomplicated assurance which was congenital rather than acquired, which she found reassuring. He was her sanctuary, her refuge. Her view of the world became synonymous with his, and that too was reassuring, liberating her as it did from the lonely self-questioning of her childhood. If her latently blossoming intellect was inhibited by such subservience, she was glad, even eager, to surrender it. It seemed a small enough price to pay for affection.

When they left university, they moved to London, where Judith took a teacher-training course in Infant Education while Patrick continued his engineering studies at a North London polytechnic. They lived frugally in a two-roomed basement flat in Kentish Town. Judith lost weight and grew her hair long, as was the fashion. Patrick introduced her to his friends and to his parents who lived in a mock-Tudor house in the stockbroker belt of Essex. His mother was a plump, flaccid woman, with pale worried eyes, who animatedly discussed recipes with Judith in the kitchen while Patrick helped his father prune roses in the garden. Judith would tie her hair back and wear sensible shoes on such visits, and this paid dividends. Their approval was made obvious when hints started to be dropped over Sunday casseroles about mortgage interest rates and the tax advantages for married couples.

The inevitability of their marriage, like the relationship which preceded it, was tacitly accepted between them. A wedding date was duly arranged and preparations put in hand. Patrick finally qualified as an engineer and took up a lucrative post in a consultancy firm in the West End. A deposit was put on a dilapidated Edwardian semi-detached in Putney. Despite this, Judith was filled with a sense of foreboding. Patrick and his family had yet to meet Cynthia.

The prospect of her mother invading the quiet tranquillity of Patrick's home and beleaguering his father with her political views made Judith shudder. It did not occur to her that while she found Cynthia's unpredictable wayward behaviour alarming, others might find it charming. She saw only the peace in her life threatened, and that she had no armour with which to defend it.

Finally, the decision was taken out of her hands. Patrick's parents, impatient perhaps at her delaying tactics, wrote directly to Cynthia, inviting her for the weekend a month before the wedding. The Friday evening before Cynthia's visit, she and Patrick drove down to Essex as usual. It was summer and the roads were clogged with evacuating traffic. Judith sat beside Patrick, watching the gleaming rooftops of the cars stretching ahead of them, and cautiously suggested that he warn his parents that allowances should be made for her mother. He glanced at her sharply. Hastily Judith explained herself.

'It's simply she . . . she can be difficult sometimes. Particularly with strangers.'

'That goes for most of us, surely?'

'Mother isn't like most people.'

The statement came out more harshly than she intended and she quickly elaborated.

'She doesn't consider how others think or feel. It's as if she enjoys antagonising them, especially if she knows they're important to me.'

'Why, for heaven's sake?'

'It's just the way she is. The way things are between us.'

Now that she attempted to articulate it, the explanation sounded hollow. Patrick, too, seemed unreceptive to her comments, as if offended by her disloyalty to her mother. He was old-fashioned about such things. Patiently, she tried to explain something of her complex relationship with Cynthia. But as she did, she felt the same old

15

confusion. She could feel the abrasive clarity of Cynthia's mind, even in her absence; the memory of it daunted her, as it always had done. Still she laboured on.

'She sounds like a character,' Patrick said when she'd finished. 'Nothing wrong in that. One must accept people as they are, not as one would wish them to be.'

By now the traffic had cleared and an open stretch of motorway lay ahead. Judith turned to look at the fleeting fields beyond the window, uncomfortably aware that it was not Cynthia's image she had disillusioned him about, but her own.

*　　*　　*

In retrospect she should have known of course that Cynthia would not betray her publicly. The weekend was an unqualified success. Cynthia arrived punctually, suitably dressed in a modest trouser suit. Over dinner she listened courteously to Patrick's father discuss the virtues of the Common Market and, after dinner, she and Patrick's mother swapped anecdotes about their children's respective babyhoods. With Patrick, too, she was politeness itself, even coquettish, as he hovered over her, decanter or ashtray in hand. It was only when they were alone, while Patrick's parents washed the supper dishes and Patrick himself had been despatched to the local pub to replenish her supply of cigarettes, only then did Cynthia become more recognisably herself.

'My God,' she said. 'How can you stand it?'

'Stand what?'

'They're so *dull*.' She hissed the word scornfully, a wary eye on the door.

'They're nice people, Mother.'

'They can afford to be. This house must be worth a hundred thousand at least. He looks like he's never done a decent day's work in his life.'

'He's a retired merchant banker.'

'There you are then.'

Cynthia stood up and moved to the window. The sun was setting, bathing the immaculate garden with its swing seat and symmetrically striped lawn in a listless marmalade haze.

'We don't belong here. No one with fire in their belly belongs here. Certainly no child of mine.'

Judith quickly rose to shut the door.

'Please don't ruin everything, Mother.'

'It's you who are doing the ruining.'

Beyond the window the sinking sun caught the flecks of grey in Cynthia's hair, making them sparkle like a halo round her head.

'And in ten years' time you'll be just like them. Smug and complacent, without an original thought in your head. Up to your knees in soft pile and soft options.'

'You underrate them, Mother. And me.'

Cynthia turned irritably, as if the conversation tired her.

'Perhaps, but if I do, you're about to prove me right, aren't you?'

'If you think that . . .' Judith hesitated, listening to the muted sounds of Patrick's parents in the kitchen . . . 'Why this polite charade that you're so delighted with it all?'

'Would you prefer it if I tell them what I really think?'

'You usually do.'

Cynthia regarded her a moment, almost as if deciding whether it was worth the trouble of continuing.

'Perhaps I thought that would make you all the more determined to go through with it. Besides, if you can't see it yourself, there's really no way I can make you, is there?'

Her tone was jaunty, as it often was when discussing anything of even passing significance.

Patrick returned and the conversation was dropped,

leaving Judith unsettled and dismayed. It was the closest she and her mother had come to a frank exchange and she was aware of a genuine anxiety in Cynthia's manner, disguised under her laconic tone. The experience was an unfamiliar one for Judith and it was that which unsettled her. Clearly she had been issued with a warning, but exactly why she was uncertain.

They had been married nearly two years before they discussed starting a family. Judith spent the first year teaching in a local infants school. The experience exhausted her. The children did not want to learn, and she quickly discovered that she did not want to teach them. It was not patience she lacked, but stamina. Until then she had always considered herself good with children, but the children who daily confronted her over Lego towers and alphabet flash cards were not like any other children she had previously encountered. They bit and spat at each other, and when she tried to intervene, would regard her with sullen and wary eyes. The little activities she painstakingly prepared for them in her own time, picture puzzles and potato printing kits, were received in obstinate silence and tossed dismissively aside. Her attempts to discipline them were met with the same insulting indifference. She would come home, trembling with spite and on the verge of tears, where Patrick would arrive to find her brooding dismally in front of the television, the supper uncooked and the bed unmade.

It was he who suggested she give it up. His own career was prospering and they no longer needed her meagre income. Besides which, there was a greater need for her at home. Patrick did not care for domesticity himself, and pointed out that it was impractical to pay someone else to cook and clean for them when Judith was more than able to do it herself. She accepted his suggestion without question. He, at least, would appreciate her endeavours.

Chapter Three

Yet when she tendered her resignation, half way through the Easter term, she felt an inexplicable apprehension.

The year preceding the baby's conception passed uneventfully. Judith devoted much of her time to decorating the house. The fittings and decor of each room were planned like a military exercise. Every shade of paint, every pattern of wallpaper was chosen to harmonise with carpets and curtains. If it was a chore, Judith did not regard it as such. For the larger jobs of wallpapering or plastering she brought in contractors, each one rigorously scrutinised and interviewed beforehand. The curtains, bedspreads and cushion covers she made herself. She became adept at needlepoint and quilted patchwork. The slow pace of her life began to tell on her figure; the lost weight was irrevocably regained. Each day melted into the one before it. It was around then she noticed that all their friends were producing children, and she was aware that she, too, wanted a child.

The certainty of this knowledge gathered momentum almost daily. She discussed the subject with Patrick, and it was decided that a last annual ski-ing holiday to Courcheval should be arranged, 'our last civilised fling of freedom' they said to their friends.

They sat on the verandah of their hotel in the twilight, watching the sun set over the mountains. The lights from the village winked at them from the shrouded valley beneath; like fairyland they said. It was at such a moment that they fell to discussing names for their as yet unborn and unconceived offspring. They decided upon Jane if a girl, and Jack if a boy. The decision was arrived at mutually, as were all their decisions.

Six weeks after their return Judith was pregnant. She told Patrick over supper, who promptly telephoned his parents. Cynthia, too, was included in the good tidings, by a postcard from Judith, which was greeted by silence. But after some weeks, when Judith was beginning to swell under her maternity smock and experience the first twinges of nausea, Cynthia finally rang. She had just found the postcard under a stack of unopened mail, she said, which was one hell of a way to discover you were about to be a grandmother. The conversation was brief and Cynthia sounded distracted. She was late for a concert, a friend was playing the viola and they were going out to a party afterwards. She did not enquire after Judith's health nor comment further on her pregnancy. Indeed, had it not been for the reference to being a grandmother, it seemed doubtful whether she had even registered the fact. As she replaced the telephone, Judith was plunged into rueful introspection. Not for the first time she acknowledged how she longed for her unborn child to be a girl. Only through a daughter could her own childhood be redeemed.

Chapter Four

At the exact moment that Judith went into labour, Cynthia was searching the kitchen for a bottle of gin. As a rule she did not drink gin late at night, but this particular evening had found her peculiarly restless and morose. A gin, she had decided, would relax her, at least sufficiently to consider going to bed, even if once there she didn't sleep. That obstacle she would overcome later. She scanned the kitchen, cluttered with unwashed saucepans and crockery, and eventually spotted the bottle propping open the pantry door. Unable to face finding the tonic, she filled the glass with tap water and bore it, together with an ashtray and a pack of cigarettes, out on to her back porch. After carefully arranging herself in a wicker chair, she lit a cigarette and took a sustained pull at the drink. She leant back in the chair, allowing what breeze there was to nudge at her face. She raised a hand to her burning cheek; she did not need a mirror to know that her face was scarlet. Every night for the last two months it had been the same. And always at night, when she was at her most vulnerable. It was a conspiracy, she thought, and promptly started to sweat.

Cynthia had been diagnosed as menopausal. Hormone therapy had been suggested if the symptoms persisted, which they had, quite perniciously, which was why Cynthia now had a hospital appointment as an outpatient the following day.

The most obvious symptom was the hot flushes; less obvious but just as persistent was the depression. 'Involutional melancholia' she had heard it described somewhere. Or perhaps she had read it. That seemed to lend it a certain inevitability which irritated her. She felt that she had so far successfully circumnavigated most of the usual pitfalls of being female. It seemed somehow unjust that she should be ensnared now, when her physical resources were so low.

On the rare occasions when she did pause to examine the cause of her depressions, which her solitary existence gave her ample opportunity to do, she knew the answer lay in the mirror. She was, quite definitely, ageing. Almost daily. Whether it was the menopause or simply a more detached eye which brought about this realisation she did not know, or particularly care. She only knew that the face which now greeted in the mirror was that of a middle-aged woman. It jolted her into a new confrontation with herself. However, she was not ready for the confrontation. She decided that she simply would not have it. She would go to the hospital and receive injections to boost her diminishing supply of hormones, and the ageing process would stop. Or at least be

curtailed, and having created a breathing space for
herself, she would prepare to make the inevitable
surrender to middle age with equanimity. This was her
plan. It seemed to her, at the time of making it,
foolproof.

Although Cynthia had accepted the diagnosis that she
was menopausal, she did not broadcast the fact. Judith
would just be embarrassed, the few remaining female
friends she had of her own age did not invite such
confidences, and for once she did not thrust it upon them.
After she had dealt with it, she would raise it, much as
she discussed her two divorces, as an event which had
occurred in the past which she had successfully overcome; she would make it sound effortless and they would
marvel at her resolve and strength of character. This, too,
had been part of her plan, though less formulated than the
other. But now she was about to be betrayed; as if to
publicly confirm the event, she was about to become a
grandmother. What was that if not a conspiracy?

Inside the house the telephone started to ring, the
sound of it ricocheting around the silent stone walls of the
garden. Sweating slightly, she quickly moved through the
sitting room to pick it up. The sound of pips greeted her,
then Patrick's voice, high-pitched and excited.

'Cynthia? I'm at the hospital. She's started.'

For a moment Cynthia's mind went blank, and then
cleared.

'I thought it wasn't due yet.'

'Yes, today. It's bang on time. Assuming she isn't in
labour for hours. They're getting her ready now, so I
thought I'd ring, keep you posted. I hope I didn't wake
you?'

His tone was half apologetic and yet jocular, for such
was their relationship.

'No, no, I'm not in bed. Are you going to stay with
her? Have you decided?'

He laughed, almost shrilly.

'That's the general idea. God knows why, I feel like a spare part already.'

Cynthia could not help a rueful smile.

'Well, if it's what she wants . . . '

'Oh quite, absolutely.'

A small pause followed while he gathered his thoughts.

'I didn't actually know it would hurt so much.'

Cynthia hesitated, trying to visualise her daughter robbed of her usual composure, writhing in the indignity of childbirth. It was not an image she could summon easily.

'She'll get through it. We all do. After all, it's not called labour for nothing'

'I suppose not. . .' He sounded dejected. 'I'd better go. She might be asking for me.'

'Yes.'

Once again Cynthia hesitated, sensing the conversation was unfinished. The gin had left a sour after-taste in her mouth. She badly needed a cigarette.

'You'll ring again, will you?'

'As soon as there's some news.' Once again that small pause. 'Trouble is, I'm no better at this sort of thing than she is.'

Without elaborating further, he hung up. Cynthia stood, the telephone in her hand. She felt a small, bitter twinge of pity for them. Children, coping with childbirth. Well, if nothing else, it would perhaps make them grow up, as it had forced her to do. She replaced the telephone and returned to her wicker chair, incredulous at her lack of charity, then tossed the thought aside. When the baby was born it would all come right. Wasn't the bond between mothers and daughters always strengthened by childbirth? She and Judith would no longer shrink from each other, their past differences would be thrown into relief by the clarity of this one common experience they now shared. She could be the sort of mother she'd never allowed herself to be. She smiled into the darkness, sipping her gin. If there was a conspiracy, it had suddenly taken on a new aspect, giving her a new and challenging role to play.

Chapter Five

Twenty minutes after the birth of her son, after Judith had been stitched and washed, and the baby weighed and examined, she was left alone with Patrick in the labour room for a few minutes. The baby lay sleeping in the basinette beside the bed. Beyond the closed doors of the room, they could hear the clatter of lift doors, voices raised in greeting as a new shift arrived. Patrick sat on the bed between her and the baby, holding her hand. He did not speak and neither did she. Instead they sat looking at the baby in preoccupied silence. Judith had not voiced her disappointment over its sex to Patrick. He was, by anyone's estimation, a beautiful, well-formed baby, his features, under the smears of blood still clinging to his face, perfectly proportioned, his complexion, unlike other newborns she had seen, not an angry purple, but a clear, almost translucent milky white. The crown of his head, where the skull bones had not yet fused together, was gently inflating in rhythm with his breathing. It struck her that she had never seen anyone so peaceful in repose.

Patrick himself had never stated a preference for his offspring's sex. 'We'll take what comes,' he had always said cheerfully whenever the subject cropped up. Despite this, he had, she observed, always referred to the unborn child as a 'he' but she restrained herself from reading anything into it of significance; after all, their much consulted pregnancy manual did the same. It was clearly just a question of syntax.

As they watched, the baby stirred, one hand resting against his cheek, briefly fluttering and then clenched, his eyes, slanting and opaquely blue, momentarily revealed, then shuttered again. Judith instantly tensed and then, as the tremor of his movement passed, relaxed again. Was this how it was going to be? Her reacting to every tiny gesture as if it implied some invisible demand that she was inexorably obliged to meet?

Patrick released her hand, stood up and stooped paternally over the baby. His face had that puffed, flushed look it often had when he was moved or awed by something. She had observed it before, in the cinema, or when he listened to certain pieces of music. He lowered a forefinger towards the baby's face, with the clear intention of stroking it. Almost immediately she froze again.

'Don't,' she said, as Patrick turned, suprised, hastily adding, 'let him sleep now. There's plenty of time for that later.'

'I only want to touch him.'

'My milk hasn't come through yet, has it? If you wake him, he might decide he's hungry.'

Patrick accepted the explanation, as she knew he would. She was after all the mother, which lent her a new unimpeachable authority. But were all mothers frightened of their newborn babies, she wondered? Somehow even thinking it gave her fear a credence, rendering it into something separate from herself, like a dry twig tapping on a window; which made her afraid in turn. Patrick sat back down on the bed beside her, loosely entwining his fingers through hers.

25

'Are you disappointed about it not being a girl?'

'No, no.'

The twig inside her head tapped like a pulse. Patrick's hand, with its familiar contours and abrasions, lay heavily on her own.

'It's all right if you want to go.'

'I don't mind staying.'

'You can come back later, at visiting. When I'm less tired. When we both are.'

'Of course.'

He kissed her, almost formally. Behind him, through the open window, she could hear a bird singing.

'Poor darling, you have been through it.'

He stood up, and bent over the baby again, but distractedly; he was anxious to be off now and spread the news.

'Is there anything you need?'

'Another nightie perhaps. And some juice of some sort.'

'Right.'

He was already thinking of what he would tell them, what it was like watching his son being born. He felt boyish and light-headed. She wanted him gone. Sensing this, he moved to the door. He would open the roof of the car on the way home, and put on a Beach Boys cassette. He would whistle and drive too fast. She wished she was going with him.

*   *   *

It was half past seven in the morning by the time Patrick got through to Cynthia. By now she was heavily asleep and received the news of her grandson with a series of incomprehensible grunts. Patrick, used to her ways, was undiscouraged, and a swimmy comprehension dawned as he ploughed on enthusiastically with details of his son's birthweight and appearance.

'And how's Judith,' she asked eventually, one hand groping on her bedside table for her cigarettes.

'Oh fine, tired you know. I'm going to see her this afternoon.'

'I'll go too.'

He hesitated for a second.

'It's husbands only, remember, for the first twenty-four hours.'

'I doubt they'll be that rigid about it.'

'No, perhaps not,' he conceded.

After saying that he would see her there, he hung up. She ceased looking for a cigarette and slumped back into bed. Later she would wash her hair and go to the café in the high street for breakfast. It was not quite a transport café, but the food was hot and plentiful and reasonably cheap. There was a young man in the café, to whom she was mildly attracted. It was not a mutual attraction, she recognised this. He was barely seventeen, and wore an ear-ring. She gave him cigarettes and in return he gave her free cups of coffee. She listened to his stories about his friends, and then she would tell him stories about herself, more exotic and less probable, and he would listen, watching her with his sharp, knowledgeable eyes, unable to reconcile the bizarre, heady images she conjured up with the broken fingernails and shabby duffel coat. Today she would tell him about her grandson and he would say 'no kidding', which he often said, and their conversation would drift on to other matters; so the event would take on its proper perspective.

*　　*　　*

Patrick's parents also received the news of their first grandchild in bed. Unlike Cynthia, they were already awake, listening to the weather forecast on the radio. After his call, they rose, showered in turn, and prepared themselves for the day ahead. It would be a busy day, there were telegrams to be sent, flowers to be ordered, baby garments to be bought and dispatched. They smiled agreeably at each other over the breakfast table. He could speak to the local vicar, he said, about arrangements for the christening. She thought for a moment and shook her head. They might have made their own plans. Best not to interfere. One must start, after all, as one means to go on.

*   *   *

There were other people on Patrick's list to phone that morning. His colleagues at work; Chris, his best friend and best man; a maiden aunt; an assortment of cousins and friends; and lastly, their neighbours. Most of the people in the street where they lived had young children. It had not been a matter of much interest when they first moved in, but as Judith's pregnancy advanced it struck them that they should form a closer alliance with their neighbours, thinking ahead to babysitting rotas and playgroups. Accordingly, their neighbours were invited in for Sunday evening wine-and-cheese parties, where first names and house keys were quickly exchanged.

It was nearly ten o'clock by the time Patrick had ticked off the last name on the list prepared for him by Judith in her neat, sloping writing. He had repeated the same soliloquy over a dozen times and the ritual of it had dampened some of his excitement. He felt restless and jaded and the house seemed almost unbearably empty. He cooked himself a plate of scrambled eggs and bacon and carried it up to the bedroom, together with a cup of tea, where he settled down to it, perched up in bed, reflecting on times past when he and Judith used to eat in bed, together, at night or in the early morning, in their basement flat in Kentish Town. It was just one of the many pleasures they had abandoned in the past two years. It was drizzling outside and the window was splashed with tiny pellets of rain, which dribbled in wrinkles down the wet surface of the glass. He watched them for a while, idly. He felt he should be doing something, something active, but he wasn't certain what. The nursery had been completed weeks before, there were no last minute chores to attend to. Judith had seen to everything. Then he remembered that he hadn't slept and felt faintly cheered. He would sleep for a while and then have lunch in the pub, where no doubt drinks would be bought for him to wet the baby's head. Afterwards, he would make his way to the hospital. He set the alarm clock for one, drew the curtains, and climbed into bed. But his sleep when it finally came, was shallow, punctured by Judith's voice shouting out in pain; her face was bloated and straining, blistered by broken blood vessels, receding and beckoning, like an accusation.

Chapter Six

It was a four-bedded ward, each one provided with a handbasin, a bedside locker and a panel of sockets, into which portable televisions and radios could be plugged. The covers on the beds were blue, flecked with white flowers; the curtains around the beds were made from a lightweight fabric of the same pattern. There was a pervading smell of antiseptic and, underneath it, discordant, the sweet smell of breast milk.

Judith had a bed by a window, for which she was grateful. The three other mothers smiled at her in bright sympathy as she was wheeled into the ward, the baby in her arms. A nurse then scooped the baby up, now tightly wrapped like a long white parcel in a hospital shawl, and bore him off through the swing door. Another nurse helped Judith into the bed, and unpacked her bag, shovelling her possessions into the bedside locker. She performed this task in silence before she straightened up, pushed a strand of hair under her cap, and asked if Judith would like to sleep; they could keep the baby in the nursery for a while. A surge of gratitude flooded through Judith. If she contrived to sleep long enough, by the time the baby was returned to her Patrick would be back for visiting time. If the baby woke, they could greet it together; if it cried, Patrick could hold it and comfort it, for she was sure he could, and that would be the first hurdle passed. As she opened her mouth to reply, she became aware of the eyes of the other mothers watching her. She now noticed all their babies in the shiny plastic basinettes at the ends of the beds. The gratitude was replaced by a sudden uncertainty, a sudden anxiety that she might be breaking some unspoken code.

'He'll sleep too, won't he? I mean, he could stay in here and we could both sleep.'

'As you like.'

The nurse disappeared, in a swish of starch. The mother in the opposite corner beamed at her reassuringly behind a barrage of pink baby cards and wilting carnations.

'Best thing. You never know what they do to them out there.'

'No, quite.'

Judith tried to assume a knowledgeable tone. But she was watching the door, already tensing herself for the baby's return.

'They're always bloody weighing them.'

Another voice piped up, from the other corner. A limp redhead with crêped, freckle-splashed forearms, was filing her nails.

'They've nothing else to do if you ask me.'

Chapter Six

Judith cast a furtive glance at the adjacent bed. An olive-skinned, raven-haired woman now lay sleeping, plump and oiled, like a melon, her hands neatly folded on her chest as if in prayer, a silver chiffon scarf tied turban-style around her head.

'Caesarian,' the redhead said, more as a point of information than one to arouse comment, and Judith made none. The women asked her if the baby was her first, and then enquired about the nature of the delivery, his weight and sex, and Judith realised that the order of the questions was clearly important, for on her reply would depend her future status in the ward. First-timers ranked, it seemed, as novices to be guided through the maternal minefield that lay ahead; only she and the woman in the nextdoor bed were first-timers, but she was a Caesarian, which, it transpired, carried its own, devalued status. Judith saw she had no choice but to succumb to the greater authority of the two women opposite, who had already produced five children between them, discounting their newborn infants. She did not resent her lowly status, for she saw in it certain definite advantages; they didn't expect her to be knowledgeable on baby matters and, indeed, would have been disappointed if she had been. She would be allowed to fail, as she was now certain that she would, in the initial handling and care of her child, and her failure could enhance the relationship of camaraderie it seemed destined they must share. In the face of her failure, they would be free to offer nuggets of matriarchal wisdom, often conflicting, but that too was comforting, cropped from their own endeavours and past mistakes. She saw all this as they talked to her, while waiting for her baby's return, and felt her fear subside. As it fell away, she fell asleep; while she slept the baby, still sleeping itself, weighed again, groomed, freshly swaddled, was wheeled to the foot of her bed, where it slumbered, less fitfully

31

than she, but as obliviously. The women fell reluctantly silent, their eyes upon their own infants, their words of advice still moist on their lips, knowing that they had just denied themselves the right to fail, inwardly bracing themselves for the approaching moment when they must put their words into practice.

Judith was not allowed to sleep for long. Three-quarters of an hour later she woke to the sound of the curtains being drawn around the bed. Another nurse, in a different uniform, a shimmering blue nylon with a label saying 'midwife' pinned on its lapel, now turned to her. She had dark hair, scraped back in a pleat under her cap, with a heavy mantle of swinging fringe; underneath, two small, raisin-like eyes peered and glimmered. Her skin looked waxen and yellow under the harsh neon lights of the ward; she seemed older than the other nurses, but this too could have been a trick of the light. She glanced briefly at Judith and stooped over the baby, long fingers probing into the small bundle of blankets.

'You are breast feeding, aren't you?'

'Yes.'

The raisin eyes were looking at the baby rather than Judith, who struggled painfully into a sitting position.

'Time to make a start, I think.'

'But my milk hasn't come through yet, has it?'

Judith involuntarily touched her breast, her anxiety returning, apprehensive that her milk had somehow invaded her while she was asleep.

'No, no. But sucking will help stimulate it, and him.'

She was holding the baby, still drunkenly asleep, one tiny arm flung out, face white, eyes tightly drawn.

'We'll just put him on for a few minutes, so you can both get the hang of it.'

She drew a chair up to the bed and sat down, the baby expertly flung over a shoulder. Judith fumbled with the buttons on her nightdress. The nurse was trying to prod

32

the baby awake, tickling the sole of his foot while simultaneously rubbing a finger over his cheek. He quivered and squirmed under her touch, his mouth fretfully setting in a determined grimace, his eyes stubbornly closed. Judith's nightdress was now open; she could see, as if from a great height, her breasts hanging beneath it, swollen and domed, crowned with the brown puckered nipples. Her cheeks flared into a scorching red and she rebuked herself sternly. It was a normal function – hundreds, thousands of women performed it daily. She dragged the right breast from the dark privacy of the brassière, and draped it over her nightdress. It hung, inert, the tip of the nipple erect.

The nurse handed her the bundle of baby. He was wearing a blue shirt, airtex, which gaped open, revealing the bloodied stump of his navel. Judith experienced a shudder of distaste. The baby was still deep in sleep, and the nurse, now standing, was pushing at his face, guiding it towards her nipple, prising his mouth apart with a forefinger.

'He seems terribly sleepy.'

'We get them worse than this.'

The raisin eyes flicked towards her, and then back at the baby. Judith felt clumsy and unco-ordinated. The infant was slack and floppy in her hands, as if drugged. The nurse started to tickle his foot again, and his eyes flickered open to gaze blearily up at Judith, before closing. She was sweating profusely. The baby's look seemed to her puzzled and resentful. The nurse pouched his cheeks between her forefinger and thumb, pushing his crumpled lips towards the vainly waiting nipple. Judith watched as if it was happening to someone else. His mouth sagged sluggishly around the unappetising nub of nipple and for an awful moment the thought occurred to Judith that he might actually choke on it. The nurse was making small encouraging sounds to the baby as she pushed and prised at his mouth. After a while her patience seemed to flag. Judith noticed for the first time that her cheeks, too, were flushed bright pink.

'It's probably the Pethedine that's making him so sleepy,' she ventured, thinking that the nurse felt the baby's failure to suckle was a personal reflection on her professional capabilities.

'Probably.'

Undeterred, she pouched the baby's cheeks again, and started to tickle at his foot. A yell of exasperation echoed dismally somewhere in the back of Judith's mind. The baby was clearly as exhausted as she, why couldn't the wretched woman see it? She shifted her position irritably, and the baby's head promptly lolled back, away from the nipple.

'Try and sit still.'

The nurse said it kindly, but with a head girl's firmness. The struggle continued in silence. Each time the same thing, the same passive rejection, as the baby slumped back, the nipple brushing lumpenly at his cheek. Eventually the nurse gave up. The surrender was quick and effortless.

'That's enough for now,' she said abruptly, 'we'll try again later.'

She swiftly folded the blankets around the baby and lowered him into the basinette. Judith sank back against the pillow in relief. The nurse made a hurried note on a chart, the curtains parted, and she was gone. Judith lay for some moments, numb, apprehensively eyeing the baby. Her mind felt empty and vacant. She felt nothing. She remained like that for some time, as if waiting for something to happen, some trigger to click inside her to release her emotions for this small human being she had created. Then she too gave up, surprised that the surrender could be so painless. She closed her eyes, then instantly opened them. The curtain was parting again, the

34

ward maid reached in, dumping a plastic tray bearing cutlery and a paper napkin, on to the trestle over the bed; the hand withdrew. Like the nurse, she barely glanced at Judith, and an acute desolation swamped her. She was sore and aching and confused and her confusion was somehow emphasised by these impassive, impersonal faces who seemed as disinclined to look at her as her baby was to suck from her. Her eyes smeared with tears of self pity. Then she realised that her breast was still exposed to the world. Quickly, she tucked it away, securely buttoning it up out of sight, her privacy, if not her pride, restored until the next round.

* * *

It turned out there was no one in the pub to buy Patrick a drink. He ordered a beer and sat on a bar stool, drinking it. Then he remembered, of course, it was a weekday, and his drinking friends only used the pub at weekends. There was one other drinker in the bar besides himself. An old woman, a plastic headscarf knotted under her chin, sitting by the unlit electric log fire, a matted mongrel dog curled at her feet. The carpet was thin and threadbare; the formica surfaces of the tables were scratched and pitted; the walls stained orange with nicotine. There was a colourless, oppressive atmosphere, which hung like a sour aftertaste over the room. He wondered why he had never observed it before. The barmaid, a distracted middle-aged woman with black pencilled eyebrows and a mauve twin-set, was drying glasses behind the bar. He smiled at her pleasantly and she smiled absently back.

'Quiet today.'

'Always is, dinner time.'

A transistor radio was playing somewhere, distantly, distortedly, its bass pulsating drearily, like a hammer. Under the army of optics there was a small strip of mirror; he could see his reflection, precise and immaculate.

'My wife's just had a baby.'

The barmaid's hands paused in the wiping.

'Lovely, smashing. Boy or girl?'

'Boy.'

'Lovely.'

'Seven pounds three ounces.'

'Smashing.'

She smiled at him, revealing a row of surprisingly even white teeth. False, he thought, and smiled back at her.

'Another beer?'

'Why not.'

'On the house this time. You've something to celebrate, haven't you?'

Behind him the old woman coughed, the dog stirred, its ears momentarily pricking up. Someone switched the transistor off. He drank his second beer in silence.

✳   ✳   ✳

They swung through the ward doors together at visiting time. Judith, sitting to attention in her bed, scented, hair sprucely combed, saw her mother and winced. She had just completed another abortive attempt at breast feeding; she wanted to be alone with Patrick, but she greeted her mother with a cry of surprised pleasure and felt a first twinge of maternal pride as Cynthia looked at the baby. Patrick, too, paused by the crib, and she watched as, together, they marvelled at her son, and her pride swelled and flowered within her.

'And he's good too,' she said, when they'd exhausted the topic of his appearance. 'All the other babies seem to do nothing but cry. He just seems happy to sleep.'

'If he causes you no more bother than that in life, you're home and dry.'

Cythia sat down heavily on the seat previously

occupied by the midwife. Inside her duffel coat pocket her fingers closed around her packet of cigarettes, forbidden in these clinical surroundings. She had come straight from the gynaecology clinic, where she had just received her first hormone injection. The sight of the baby had stirred her into an unfamiliar compassion. She looked over at Judith, composed and matronly, reclining against her bank of pillows, pink and frothy and full of pride, the role of daughter to mother accomplished, it seemed, in one, silken transition. Her attention was caught by a nurse hovering uncertainly in the doorway, looking in their direction. Another one joined her and a whispered conversation took place. They seemed to be discussing Judith, or perhaps the presence of Cynthia herself. She glared at them, defying them to challenge her, and they withdrew. Patrick and Judith were talking, discussing how his parents had received the news of their grandchild, and about what food Patrick could prepare for himself that night. She watched them, their youthful faces turned earnestly to each other in attentive intimacy. Her fingers tightened around the packet of cigarettes.

*　　*　　*

After they'd gone, the mothers in the ward took out their knitting and exchanged anecdotes about their visitors or lack of them. Later the babies began to rouse and their mothers heaved themselves out of bed and waddled through the swing doors, pushing the baby trolleys before them. The baby now had his face turned towards Judith, his features elongated and magnified through the rippled plastic wall of his crib. As she watched, a plume of white vomit bubbled on to his lower lip. A trickle of alarm spread through Judith. She glanced around helplessly, but all the other mothers were out of the ward. Only the 'Caesarian' remained, in her prayer-like pose of sleep. Judith struggled out of the bed and instantly recoiled as a hot, wet pain shot upwards between her legs. Propping herself on the bed, she cautiously limped towards the sleeping baby. The froth on his lip was now dripping down his chin, coming to rest in a milky pool under his cheek. She lingered, frozen by indecision, before limping back to press the bell which would summon a nurse. The ward was silent now. An eternity seemed to pass before a nurse appeared, yet again a different one, a student nurse this time in a red striped uniform. Judith gestured towards the baby, embarrassed at her own inadequacy, tumbling the words out.

'I wasn't sure what to do. I think he's been sick.'

'I'll see to it.'

The nurse trundled the baby off without a backward glance. Judith looked out of the grubby window. Perhaps she should have gone too, to help with the baby. But the nurse had not given her the chance to offer. The thought floated into her mind that the nurse, like the midwife before her, seemed inexplicably embarrassed by something, but at that moment the ward doors opened and the redhead returned, with a flurry of fleshy forearms and muttered abuse about nursery nurses with dirty fingernails; the thought, such as it was, shrank and evaporated.

During the course of the afternoon flowers started to arrive. Soon Judith's locker, like all the others, was covered with ribboned bouquets and greeting telegrams. At one point the midwife returned, with the clear intention of resuming the breast feeding attempts, but Judith, spying her as she entered, promptly feigned sleep. The midwife dithered undecidedly by the bed for a moment before departing. Judith opened her eyes and smiled at her sleeping infant. The old feeling of alliance was renewed; once more they were in league. The idea faintly invigorated her, compensating for her discouragement over his feeding and disappointment over his sex.

Chapter Six

She looked at the ward clock. There were still two hours to go until the next visiting time. Some of her cheerfulness ebbed. The midwife was bound to return again, and next time would not be so easily outmanoeuvred.

❖   ❖   ❖

When Cynthia had visited the café that morning the boy had been there, but was too busy to speak to her. She returned there that afternoon, after her visit to the hospital. As she entered, he grinned at her over the expanse of tables and a moment later he slid into the bench in front of her, a mug of coffee in each hand. She provided him with a cigarette and a light, then pulled the ashtray into the centre of the table so that it was exactly between them. After these preliminaries were accomplished, Cynthia told him about the baby.

He did not, as she had anticipated, listen politely and then change the subject, but listened with an absorbed and quite obviously genuine interest. He asked about Judith and Patrick and whom the baby took after and what colour its hair was and whether it was to be breast fed or bottle fed and generally confounded her with the appropriateness of his questions and his grasp of the answers. He liked babies and was looking forward to having one of his own. He asked about Judith's babyhood, she told him it was all so long ago she couldn't remember. But she did remember. The sight of her infant grandchild, while he did not especially physically resemble Judith as a baby, had brought the memories back. Not just of Judith as an infant, but as a toddler, and later, as a little girl.

She had always been a secretive, placid child, easily moved to tears and eager to please. She washed dishes and vacuumed, and shopped and did her homework and watched television in measured, sensible doses. She was altogether a very sensible little girl. At thirteen she got her first period and developed several severe crushes on various pop stars, glimpsed fleetingly on television, usually the drummer or base guitarist in a band rather than the lead singer, as if by somehow being more undeserving they deserved her attention more. She joined postal fan clubs and followed her idols' activities in various teenage journals, and when she was fourteen she grew out of it. She put aside her pin-up posters and turned her attention, equally seriously and methodically, to her O-levels. Through all these prudent, predictable years, she remained secretive and obedient. She was not the daughter Cynthia thought she would have, and they both knew it. In an irritable moment, Cynthia had once told her so.

'Say something for heaven's sake. Say No. Shout at me. Don't just accept everything!'

But Judith had accepted. She accepted her mother's anger and frustration as a fact of life, which indeed is what it had become. Cynthia often felt she was the child, being tolerated by an indifferent, worldly adult. It was she who went to Judith in the night when her insecurities gathered like shadows around her. She would cling on to Judith, wrapping herself around her plump, warm body, and Judith would stroke her hair until the shadows retreated and she could sleep again.

These memories of Judith rippled and drifted in her mind's eye while the boy talked. He said something, and paused, obviously waiting for her to speak. She knew if she waited long enough he would prompt her and he did.

'You must bring him in here.'

'Who?'

'The baby.'

'Oh yes. Yes.'

'People'll think he's yours.'

He grinned at her, giving the impression he was winking.

'They'll think, hello, she's been having a good time with some bloke. Whenever I see a baby with an older woman I always think that.'

'Really?'

'First thing that comes to mind.'

She considered it a moment.

'Some women actually plan it that way you know, plan to have babies late in life.'

'Not you though. Which is why people'd think it must be a love child, see?'

She digested this, thinking ahead to the impression she would create, pushing the baby out in its pram.

'I doubt my daughter would let me out alone with it.'

'Doesn't trust you, eh? She's that type, is she?'

He was watching her closely, a fleck of tobacco on his upper lip.

'She's what I've made her, I suppose.'

She said it and wondered in surprise why she had, when she hadn't consciously thought it before. Some customers came in and the boy left her. She lit another cigarette and looked out of the window. A girl was walking along the street, a toddler clutching on to her hand. She was laden down with shopping; with her free hand she pushed a plaid basket on wheels, such as old women push. Cynthia watched her until she was out of sight and ordered another coffee, which she knew would provide the boy with the excuse he needed to return to her.

*   *   *

That same afternoon the sun shone briskly and cheerlessly on the Essex back garden. Patrick's father mowed the lawn and his mother, a checkered travelling rug over her knees, sat watching him from a deckchair. She thought about the baby, crawling on the travelling rug on the lawn. She wondered whom he took after, Patrick or Judith, and decided either would be nice. She looked at her husband, frail and taut-backed, marching away from her with the lawnmower, his shirt sodden wet with perspiration. She thought perhaps he might be overdoing it, but refrained from saying so. Her thoughts were brief and disconnected and eventually she dozed. She dreamt she was sweeping a brown cord carpet, much like the one in the summer house. The broom was soft and yielding, not stiff-bristled as it should have been, and the carpet kept expanding as she brushed, until it became as large as the garden itself. Still she brushed at it, ineffectually, tirelessly, and grew quite panicked as she realised she could never get it finished. She woke to see her husband, blotched and pink, breathlessly looming over her, wanting his tea. The garden, freshly mowed, smelt sweet; the sun had gone in. She rose, stiff-kneed, pushing the travelling rug to one side. She would make tea and telephone Patrick to find out when they could visit the baby.

Chapter Seven

'It's just not happening. He's just not interested.'

'Perhaps they're giving him the bottle when you're not looking.'

It was the evening visiting time. Patrick and Judith were discussing in hushed but intense overtones her attempts at breast feeding.

'But he's always here, in here, with me. Except when

they change his nappy, which only takes a minute. They wouldn't have time.'

'Haven't you changed him yourself yet?'

'I think the idea is I rest today.'

'Can't you ask someone to help you with the feeding?'

'I told you, someone does help me. A midwife.'

'What does she say about it?'

'Nothing. Nothing much anyway. None of them do.'

They stared at the baby, mesmerised and perplexed. The voices of the other visitors vibrated around them.

'Anyway,' said Judith matter of factly, 'if he's not latching on to the breast, he's not likely to latch on to the bottle, is he?'

'Latch on?'

'It's what they call it. Latching on.'

'Well, if he's hungry he'd cry, surely? That's what babies do, isn't it?'

'Judging by the others.'

They looked around at the other babies, and back at their own.

'They're not worried are they – the nurses? So why are you?'

'I'm not.'

'Well then.'

They fell silent. She knew she wasn't worried, she was irritated, at her clumsiness when she held the baby, and at her helplessness over feeding it, and now her irritation extended to Patrick, for not recognising it.

'The other mothers have had the same problem. They told me so. They said it all sorts itself out. Once I get confident, so will the baby.'

'There you are.'

'I just think the nurses could be more ... open about it. Not make you feel so wretched.'

Her voice shook slightly, and he took her hand.

'You're just letting it get on top of you. You don't think you're getting the blues, do you?'

He looked at her sharply. They had read about post-natal depression in the pregnancy manual. It had seemed then highly unlikely, meriting only a clinical and passing interest. A case history had been cited in detail of a mother suffering from post partum blues. They had read it curiously, dispassionately, safe in the knowledge it was happening to someone else. Now they looked at each other with a new apprehension.

'No. No.' Judith said eventually, and the firmness of her reply comforted them both. They talked of other things for a while, of letters that needed writing and when they would register the birth. Finally Patrick said that maybe he should hold the baby, and, curbing her instinct to rebut him in case they should unnecessarily disturb his sleep, Judith agreed. Patrick plucked the baby out of the warmth of his shroud of blankets and cradled him in his arms. The baby blinked up at him drowsily and they giggled at his expression. After a few minutes he lapsed into sleep again and together they put him back into his basinette and Judith reminded Patrick to prepare the sterilising unit for their return and told him where she wanted it put in the kitchen. So the visiting hour passed.

Out of the corner of her eye, as they talked, Judith saw two nurses, one of them the night sister on the incoming shift, watching them through the glass porthole of the ward doors. They stood in silence, watching, before withdrawing out of her view. It seemed to her they were moved by the sight of Patrick holding the baby, and she felt another small flush of pride in the fact that they were now, quite recognisably, a family.

The ward was settling down for the night. The centre light had been switched out so that each bed was illuminated by its own individual pool of light, provided by a small low-wattage, overhanging lamp. All around Judith babies suckled and champed at breasts. In her corner the redhead brushed her teeth with mechanical, studied concentration. The night sister, black and languid and unsmiling, was trudging around the ward pushing the drugs trolley. She approached Judith bearing a plastic beaker of iron and vitamin tablets which she placed on the locker, in a small clearing between telegrams and flowers.

'Are you going to keep the baby tonight? Or put him in the nursery?'

She had an imposing ring of keys clipped on to her belt, which she fingered and fiddled with as she spoke, like worry beads. Judith promptly looked to the other mothers for guidance and perceived, or so she thought, a small nod of assent.

'If it's no trouble . . . '

The night sister blinked at her, as if trying to fathom some hidden meaning behind the words. Finding none, she moulded her features into an approximation of a smile and returned to her drugs trolley. A few moments later a nurse came and wheeled the baby out. Judith still didn't know where the nursery was. Apart from two cautious and painful excursions to the toilet, she had yet to penetrate what lay behind the swing doors of the ward.

*   *   *

She could hear the babies crying in the night, far away, under the hum of the hospital central heating generator. She wondered if hers was amongst them, and, if he *was* crying, whether she would recognise him; but then recollected that she hadn't heard him cry at all yet, even at the birth, so there was no reason why she should. Now and again one of the babies in the ward whimpered, and a mother, grimly reluctant, would hoist herself out of her

sleep and attend to the ritual of changing and feeding and
the ward would fall silent again until the next intrusion.
Judith wished she'd asked for a sleeping pill. Her mind,
agile and relentlessly alert, sprang over the events of the
day and preceding night, reliving odd irrelevant details,
while the more acute moments seemed to dissolve under
her scrutiny. She realised she was hungry and made a
mental note to ask Patrick to bring her in some biscuits.
Under her nightdress she grasped a handful of slack,
disgorged stomach. She would forgo the biscuits; she
must not put on any more weight. When she got home
she'd diet and exercise. Perhaps she and Patrick would
take up jogging, as he had often declared they should.
They could buy tracksuits and jog around the park in the
evenings, and call in at the pub for a lager on the way
home. Then she remembered the baby, and realised that
such spontaneous activities, however trivial, were no
longer possible. Another realisation followed it; that it
was *she* who had usually curtailed such activities in the
past. She sighed into the night and the sigh floated over
the silent ward, like escaping gas. Had she married a
different man, he might have thrown such arguments in
her face, as her mother used to. Despite herself, she
would have been forced into a participation, however
grudging, and learnt to shrink less from the unfamiliar
and regard it, as others clearly did, as a challenge which
might extend and liberate. It was not disloyalty to Patrick
which made her think this, but a sudden, awesome sense
of her inhibitions; of that prudent, pragmatic common
sense which had dogged her footsteps since infancy, and
which now ran, like a moat, around her marriage,
isolating and manacling them both. The baby then took
up its own position in her imaginings, as a drawbridge
they could lower over the moat, over which they could
jointly navigate a route to the world beyond. The idea
crystallised and blossomed in her mind, like a point on

a horizon, thrown into detail by a magnifying lens. Besides, jogging was probably not such a good idea, there were sure to be muggers in the park.

*   *   *

As he passed the nursery that night en route to bed, Patrick paused, opened the door, switched on the light and glanced inside. The room was bathed in hazy yellow, emanating from the wallpaper and curtains. The cot, gleaming and freshly painted, stood against one wall, piled high with neatly folded baby clothes. A playpen stood under the window, a knitted teddy bear, made by Judith, was crookedly propped in a corner, an abacus in the other. The thick pile carpet was soft under his feet. The room overlooked the garden, and he crossed now to the window, looking out into the darkness. He could just discern the symmetrical grey rectangle of his lawn beneath him and, stretching away on either side, the other, identical, rectangles of the neighbouring gardens. He could also see himself, reflected in the window, surrounded by the yellow haze of the room beyond. Judith had suspended a mobile above the playpen, six brown felt teddy bears, which slowly revolved and floated in the draught from the open door. He touched the mobile with a forefinger, and its momentum increased, the bears dizzily joggling and spinning. He thought of the baby occupying the room; lying in the playpen, gazing up at the mobile. He thought of himself in the room, on a night like this one, playing with the baby or putting it to bed. He thought these things not with any particular sense of excitement or anticipation but indolently, in passing, surprised that he felt nothing more.

His mind dwelt briefly on his own childhood, comfortable and judicious; he speculated on why it was that, at the age of twenty-eight, married and now a father, he should still regard the house in Essex as his home. The notion unsettled him, as it always did. He recollected his reaction on first hearing the news that Judith was pregnant, how he had almost immediately sprung up to telephone his parents. The crucial events in his life, it suddenly occurred to him, had always made him react this way, as if they had to be endorsed or approved by his parents, before he could assess their value to himself. The idea of this unsettled him too. He recalled then the look in Judith's eyes as he jumped up to make the telephone call – impatient, yet resigned. She had worn that same look when he had asked to hold the baby that evening.

He laid his forehead on the cold glass of the window. He could see his own eyes now, glittering back at him, two piercing pin-pricks of light embedded in the blackness of his silhouette. He stared at himself a moment before abruptly crossing back to the door. His mouth felt terribly dry. If there was enough milk he would make himself a hot drink before going to bed. As he passed, the bears on the mobile bobbed and dived at him, and after he'd gone their momentum lasted for a while, until eventually it dissipated and they hovered, sluggish and then motionless, except for an occasional shiver as the vibrations in the air around them eddied and rippled in the silent room.

Chapter Eight

At six in the morning the curtains in the ward were flung back and a tea trolley clanked up the aisle between the beds. The mothers lay hunched in silent protest. Judith blinked the sleep from her eyes to see the night sister standing over her, the crisp white square of her apron stiffly erect, as if to attention.

'So. How did we sleep?'

'Very well. Thank you.'

'We fed the baby in the night for you. You were sound asleep so we thought it best not to disturb you.'

Judith blinked again, trying to focus her thoughts.

'How ... ? How did you feed him? He was hardly feeding at all yesterday.'

'Oh, we put a tube down him, from his nose into his stomach. It's quite routine until a baby's suckling reflex is established.'

'I see.'

'Just a few mls of diluted milk, to give him some nourishment.'

'I see,' she said again.

'We'll take the tube out after the morning feed so you can try him on the breast again. They don't suck as well if the tube's still in.'

'Thank you.'

The night sister leant over and hooked an arm under Judith's, levering her forward so she could plump the pillows. Her actions were hasty and decisive, like her manner.

'Feeding often takes a few days to get going with newborns, there's nothing to be concerned about.'

'I'm not really.'

She relaxed her grip on Judith's arm, who rolled back against the mountain of pillows.

'We'll bring the baby back as soon as we can.'

The keys jangled as she walked briskly away. Judith lay, drowsily ruminating on the conversation. She could still feel the night sister's touch upon her arm. She must have frowned, for the woman in the opposite bed called out to her, a cup and saucer poised in each hand.

'My second one was a devil like that . . . to feed . . . took
him days to get the hang of it.'

'Oh?'

'It's all these drugs if you ask me. Epidurals and
what-nots. It slows them down.'

'I didn't have an epidural.'

The woman sipped her tea and grimaced at the taste.

'You want to watch them giving him that artificial stuff
though. Artificial milk. He might get a liking for it.'

'But mine's not come through yet.'

'Glucose and water. You tell them, if he needs food,
to give him that, it's quite enough for the next day or
two.'

She had large, owl-like spectacles, which gave her a
deceptively studious look.

'I will. Thank you.'

The woman nodded sagely, and returned to her tea.
Judith closed her eyes, knowing that when she opened
them the baby would be back with her again: the day
would begin in earnest.

*   *   *

It was nearly nine before she next woke. She opened her
eyes, to see, not the baby, but another face, grinning
impishly down at her. It was Chris, their best man and
Patrick's best friend. It took her an instant to recognise
him and, when she did, she sat up in startled dismay.

'Chris . . . '

'Hello, little mother.'

'It's not visiting is it? Did they let you in?'

'I didn't ask. The lawyer's mind, you see, eternally
forewarned and forearmed. I rang Patrick last night, got
him to tell me where you were, what ward, the floor and
so forth, and just breezed in like I was a doctor. I was
tempted to wear a white coat but I couldn't lay my hands
on one.'

Chapter Eight

He was wearing a suit and tie. Even without the white coat he could easily have been a doctor. He had the same assurance, the same stature and gait. Judith cast a rapid look around the ward. The mothers were still dozing, only the redhead was feeding her baby, squinting short-sightedly in their direction. Chris followed her gaze.

'Whoops. Better get a bit of privacy, I think.'

As she watched helplessly, he tugged the curtains around the bed.

'Chris . . . you'll get me into trouble.'

'Never.'

He stood, generous and unfamiliar, the curtains swinging behind him.

'So where is the little chap?'

'Being fed in the nursery.'

'I thought you were feeding him yourself?'

'I am. It's not . . . established yet.'

'How formal you make it sound.'

She smiled wanly. She felt pale and insipid. He had never seen her without make-up before.

'Since I pass this way to work I thought I'd pop in. Then I can tell everyone I was the first to see him, aside from you and Patrick, of course. Give me something to gloat about.'

She smiled again, politely, and he smiled airily back.

'I feel like the Last of the Mohicans. The last of the old crowd to be childless. Not to mention wifeless.'

She thought of him at the wedding, in his role of best man, reading out the telegrams. He had told her then, whispering it in her ear as they danced under the marquee in the Essex backgarden, that she had the right body for bearing children. He had placed a hand on her buttock and grasped it, like checking fruit for ripeness, squeezing it, not sensually but absently, his eyes on one of the bridesmaids. She had removed his hand, and promised

51

him that if and when she produced a child, he could be
the godfather. He had laughed at the idea, the way he did,
with gusto, head thrown back, his presence somehow
obscuring her own.

'You must go. I'll never hear the end of it if you're
found.'

'When will I get to see him?'

'At visiting time, like everyone else.'

'Spoilsport.'

He plucked up a telegram and scanned it idly.

'I come empty handed, I'm afraid. Flowers might have
given the game away.'

'It doesn't matter.'

She was straining, listening for the swing of the ward
doors signalling the entry of a nurse.

'Does it feel any different? Having a baby?'

'Why should it?'

He replaced the telegram on the locker.

'In my experience it changes people. Men as well as
women.'

'I don't see why it should.'

'Neither do I. But I have the evidence of my own eyes,
not to mention several neglected friendships. You'll see,
from now on all your single friends will lose their appeal.
You'll hanker only after couples with babies, so you can
swap stories about nappy rash and potty training.'

'Don't be silly.'

He raised an eyebrow, his expression arrogant and
confident. Yet she felt it was *she* who should be
reassuring him.

'We'll see,' he said and stooping, he brushed her cheek
with his lips. His chin felt rough. He rested a hand on her
shoulder; that too felt rough.

'Goodbye, little mother.'

'Come again. With Patrick perhaps.'

'Safety in numbers, eh?'

Chapter Eight

His lips twitched in another smile. Before she could reply he parted the curtains and stepped through them. She reached into her bedside locker for her compact mirror. Her face was flushed and excited. She didn't look as bad without make-up as she had thought.

She'd heard about Chris from Patrick, long before she first came to meet him. They had been at school together, and later, while Patrick went to Sheffield to study engineering and Chris was at Cambridge, reading law, they kept in close touch. Prior to Chris's visit to the hospital she had always thought their friendship had been one-sided; that is to say, on Patrick's side. He spoke of Chris with a mixture of awe and excitement. It was always Chris who took pride of place in his stories. Judith knew, even before she met him, his taste in music and literature and his love of early Hollywood musicals. She knew what size shirts he wore, the jokes he told, and how he told them. She knew also that she disliked him.

She was surprised she could dislike someone before meeting them, and equally surprised that she could feel so negative about someone Patrick was so clearly fond of. It was not out of jealousy that she felt this – at least not jealousy for the relationship he shared with Patrick. It was subtler: just the sound of his name made her feel tired. His days, compact, industrious, brimming with a multitude of activities, made hers seem vapid and mundane in comparison.

When they had finally met one Saturday lunchtime in a pub off the Fulham Road, she'd been waspish and withdrawn. But Chris, if he understood the cause of her taciturn silence, was undeterred. He directed his attention on her like a searchlight, stripping her of her usual reserve. She found herself talking openly and articulately. He seemed impressed by her, and she discovered herself rallying, wittily, audaciously. She had become an unfamiliar version of herself, animated and lovely. She told herself later that she behaved like this for Patrick, out of respect for their friendship, but wondered why she felt the need to excuse it.

They saw him often after that, at their house or the homes of mutual friends, or at his cottage on an Oxfordshire hillside. Invariably he would have a girl in tow, usually a different one but with a sameness about her. He seemed anxious for Judith's good opinion of the girls, and, flattered, she gave it. It gave her a satisfying sense of value, of permanence in the face of their transience. He was always respectful to her, but somehow familiar. They drank out of the same glass and teamed up in Monopoly. He regarded her as one of the boys, as he often said, but never let her forget she was a woman. It was a convincing combination. But the three of them made a perfect combination, as they had often agreed. She thought of these things in her hospital bed, and pondered on his visit. He had seemed anxious when he spoke of their friendship and the prospect of the baby intruding on it. She smiled: the thought of this gratified her.

Later, the baby was returned to her by the midwife, and another attempt at breast feeding began. The baby was less sleepy now, but as half-hearted as ever about feeding. He peered at the nipple curiously, almost regretfully. The midwife cajoled and encouraged him, crumpling his lips around the nipple and Judith felt his tongue, moist and flicking, glancing over its tip. Her feeling of distaste returned and deepened. After a few minutes the midwife suggested that he didn't seem hungry, he was probably satisfied by the tube feed earlier that day. Relieved, Judith stowed away her breast and the baby was replaced in his cot. He was facing towards her again, his cheek squashed against the sheet; she could see his eyes, two murky blue slits, drooping and blinking at her, behind the plastic wall of the crib. There was an impression on the side of his nose, like a small rectangular burn, where the tube had been taped on. She looked at him for a while, thinking of his tongue teasing at her nipple. The sheets felt clammy and damp on her legs. She decided a salt bath might refresh her.

When she returned from the bathroom there was a woman sitting on the bed, leaning over the baby, crooning at it. She wore an orange dressing gown, quilted and nylon, and no slippers. As Judith approached, she turned to greet her. She was toothless, or gave the impression of being so, her hair short, strawlike and greasily grey, standing out in clumps around her skull.

'Just having a peek, you don't mind, do you?'

'Of course not.'

Judith crouched, flinching, to stack her towel and washing bag inside her locker. The woman watched her, eyes wide and shiny, giving her a startled look.

'Boy or girl?'

'Boy.'

'Oh.'

Her lips clamped together in a thin, wet line. Judith sat on the opposite side of the bed, one hand resting on the crib.

'Mine's down in the unit. The special unit. He's not too well.'

'Oh. I'm sorry.'

'These things are sent to try us.'

One of her eyes suddenly shot sideways, as if catching sight of something out of the window. Disconcerted, Judith rose from the bed and busied herself with her flowers. The woman was older than most of the other mothers, in her early forties at least. Her finger-nails were bitten down to the quick, the fingers themselves scabbed and discoloured with nicotine.

'Do they know what's wrong with him?'

'Not yet. If they do, they're not saying.'

'I'm sure he's in good hands.'

'Oh, the best. The best.'

The woman said it mechanically, one eye rolling alarmingly towards the ceiling. Behind her, Judith could see the other mothers, intent and watching.

'Better go. The devil makes work for idle hands.'

The woman rose, the stale smell of blood wafting around her. She grinned toothlessly in the general direction of Judith, and limped out of the ward.

'You want to watch that one.'

The mother in the bed opposite said it, softly, her eyes on the retreating orange dressing gown.

'What's the matter with her baby?'

The mother glanced sharply at the door, where a nurse now stood checking a clipboard, before throwing back her bedclothes and shuffling towards Judith.

'She tried to drown it.'

The owl spectacles flashed and glinted in the light from the window.

'In the ladies lavatory at Victoria Station.'

Judith stared at her, uncomprehendingly.

'I heard about it on my first night. I couldn't sleep and I was having a cigarette in the day room. The night sister was telling a doctor all about it. They were in the corridor outside, the door was open and I heard the whole thing.'

The glasses flashed again.

'It seems she delivered it herself, down the loo. They found her wandering around the station in a dreadful state.'

'What happened to the baby?'

'They found him too. Alive but only just. Brain death, the doctor said. Total brain death. Infection and that. It's on some kind of machine in intensive care.'

'That's terrible. Terrible.'

'We're not supposed to know. No one is. Even the nurses don't know.'

Judith looked down at her baby's face, ashen with sleep. The eyes behind the owl spectacles followed her glance and they stared at the infant in silent, bitter bewilderment.

'She's educationally subnormal. You know, ESN. God knows why she wasn't sterilised years ago.'

'But why did she do it?'

'She didn't want him, did she?'

Judith shook her head slightly.

'Terrible. How terrible.'

'She's in a side ward but she keeps wandering about, talking to everyone. And singing. You know that song 'Save all your kisses for me'? She sings it over and over. Gives me the shivers.'

And the mother shivered, as if cold.

'I've never heard of anything so awful.'

'Well, I'd keep an eye on her if I was you. Keep her where you can see her. Someone who can do that, they can do anything, can't they?'

The owl glasses wagged at her a second before their owner shuffled back to her corner. Judith climbed into bed, drawing up her knees tightly, looking at the baby. The bed was shaking slightly; she realised she was trembling.

Chapter Nine

On his way to visit Judith at the hospital that afternoon, Patrick crashed the car. He had paused at some lights and, as they changed, let the clutch up too sharply and felt a deadening crunch as his bumper collided with that of the car in front. Both cars suffered only slightly from the impact and Patrick promptly accepted liability. But as he continued on his way he felt rattled and nervous. He prided himself on his driving and the fact that he had, until now, never had an accident, at least not one which was his fault. If he claimed on his insurance he would lose his no-claims bonus. The thought aggravated and needled him, and he drove more slowly, fumbling with the gear change. Then he decided that it was just bad luck, bad luck that the car had been so close and that the lights had changed when they had. His foot pressed down on the accelerator pedal again. Anyway, it was only a graze on the bumper, only a very minor imperfection.

He was passing the sister's office in the corridor outside the ward when a nurse suddenly darted out in front of him. She was young, in a red uniform. She looked flustered and anxious, and she caught his arm, breathlessly looking up at him.

'Mr Fielding? The paediatrician would like a word with you.'

It happened before he had time to think. She led him into the sister's office. He saw a room, small and grey and lined with books. There was one window in the room, a square skylight through which a patch of sky, cloudless and blindingly white, winked down at him, causing him to squint and narrow his eyes. The paediatrician was a middle-aged man, with gold-rimmed, half-moon glasses. He was small and thin and unsmiling. He reminded Patrick, inexplicably, of his father. He sat down and, as the paediatrician spoke the words, felt his mind emptying. He looked up at the square patch of sky. Distantly, he could hear someone singing 'Save all your kisses for me'. He felt his mouth go dry. His hands, resting on the corduroy of his trousers, felt numb and leaden. The square patch of light was drifting and weaving in front of him, as if no longer anchored by the walls of the room. The paediatrician was speaking slowly now, and unwillingly. Questions stirred in the emptiness of his mind and receded. His eyes blurred. He caught a look of impersonal tenderness crossing the face of the paediatrician before he bowed his head and wept.

Judith sat waiting, her eyes on the ward door. She concentrated on it, willing it to open, for she had promised herself that the next time it did she would see Patrick. It was unlike him to be late. Perhaps he had decided, after all, to call in at the office on his way. She wrenched her eyes from the door. Mercifully, the baby was sleeping again; visitors were congregating around the other three beds, their backs turned towards her. The redhead was surrounded by three, fuzzy, redheaded children, sitting raggedly about her bed in gloomy silence, their eyes on the clock above the window. Judith looked back at the door. Her thoughts turned briefly to Cynthia, and her unexplained visit to the hospital outpatients department the previous day. If she was ill, why not say so, why make such a mystery out of it? But then, mystery, like drama, was the stuff of her mother's life: she was hardly likely to change now. In the end she'd say what, if anything, was wrong with her. Judith only had to wait, as she always did. The ward doors suddenly sprang apart; a man entered, glancing around at the beds and clusters of visitors. He was small but walked like someone who had been tall but had shrunk slightly with age. He wore a tweed suit, with a row of pens sticking out of the breast pocket. His face was thin and strained; on his nose rested a pair of gold, half-moon glasses. He looked at her for a second, one finger hooked in a waistcoat pocket. His eyes then shifted to settle abstractedly on the baby at the foot of the bed. Behind him the ward doors opened again. The raisin-eyed midwife appeared, touched his arm, and together they went out, the doors springing shut behind them.

Judith looked up at the clock. The visiting hour was nearly half over. It was really too bad of Patrick. Perhaps she should ring home, make sure he was on his way. She'd seen a mobile, coinbox telephone in the corridor, immediately outside the ward; she could use that. She pushed back the sheets and swung her legs out of the bed. Her back was now to the door. She stretched her feet down, sliding them across the strip of floor by the bed, searching for her slippers. She did not see the ward doors open. She did not see Patrick's anguished face, or the dread in his eyes. She did not see the paediatrician grasp him by the arm and guide him relentlessly down the long polished aisle of floor towards her bed. But she heard the sound of the curtain hooks, swishing along the runner, and turned to see her husband and the middle-aged man she had noticed entering the ward a moment before, standing, walled in by the swaying curtains, one on each side of the baby's crib. She noticed then Patrick's face, smeared with tears, and the twig of fear sharply returned, not tapping this time, but beating against the sides of her head. Her mind at that moment seemed to leave her body, to soar upwards, towards the ceiling. The blood throbbed and pounded in her ears. Something inside her gathered, string-like and tautening, into a small, hard fist, clenched and ready to strike. She felt with the clarity of complete conviction that she had been preparing for the unknown terror of this moment all her life. It had always been there, behind every corner, obscured by triviality and the years. She thought this in the space of perhaps three seconds, as her body on the bed squared itself for the assault, and her detached and floating mind mustered its defences.

'What is it?' she breathed. 'What's happened?'

Patrick seemed about to speak, but the man gestured

him into silence. He moved around the bed, circling it, as she watched, bright-eyed in fear. He sat down next to her. He smelt of aftershave, his hands, manicured and unblemished, rested on the bed between them.

'I'm a paediatrician, Mrs Fielding. Do you know what that is?'

'Yes.'

He spoke quietly, calmly, as if to still the rage within her. As he spoke, he removed the gold spectacles from his nose, where she could see etched on either side two small, pink indentations.

'I have to tell you, I'm afraid, that your son is going to be a little bit slow.'

Beside her Patrick suddenly sobbed, one hand catching his mouth, as if stifling a cough.

'Don't look at your husband, Mrs Fielding. I want you to look at me. Please.'

A hand, cool and smooth, was placed over her own. Above her, her mind, armoured and vigilant, tirelessly pulsated; sifting and analysing, amputating her thoughts before exploding them like a dozen fire crackers inside her head.

'What's the matter with him?'

'He's suffering from a condition called Down's syndrome. I don't know if you know what that is?'

She shook her head as her mind raced and locked into gear. Syndrome. She thought of something circular, in perpetual motion, like ripples forming around a stone as it lands on the surface of water, ceaseless, swirling downwards, pulling its edges towards its own centre of gravity, in an endless pirouetting spiral.

Patrick was rocking silently in the chair next to her, his hands over his face, emitting small gasping sobs.

'Don't look at your husband, Mrs Fielding. I want you to look at me. Only at me.'

She jerked her head back to the paediatrician, where his

eyes, soft and liquid, held hers. He opened his mouth to speak, but Patrick's voice, harsh and insistent, lashed out.

'Tell her, for God's sake, tell her. He's a mongol. A mongol.'

A veil lifted. She was weightless suddenly. Her body floated up to meet her mind. An overwhelming repugnance hit her, like nausea. Behind the veil, understanding gleamed, incipient and insidious. The slant eyes, the embarrassed faces of the nurses, the baby's drugged, drunken sleep. The dismal attempts at feeding. His wet tongue, flicking over her nipple. The images swam before her; the twig fell silent: her fear shrivelled and contracted and was gone. The paediatrician was addressing her again.

'I want you to tell me exactly what you're thinking. What you're feeling. Don't look at your husband, only at me. Do you understand?'

She nodded and he waited. Her mind severed itself from her body once again, jettisoning into a pallid remembrance. She had worked with a mongol when she was a student in the summer vacations. She had worked as a waitress in a small café and the mongol, a teenager, had worked in the kitchen, washing dishes. She thought of his features, flattened into a mask of idiocy. She thought of the lidless incisions of his eyes, staring dully out of the putty-coloured flesh. She thought of her revulsion at the dry, flaking touch of his hands, and at his round, lolling tongue. She thought of his walk, shambling and unco-ordinated and of her exasperation at the tiresome vapidity of his mind. She thought of the spreading wet patch in front of his trousers and how, giggling, they had speculated on whether it was dishwater or something else. She then thought of the way he had squawked in delight as she swatted flies and how he had danced and twirled in the patches of sunlight which splashed through the window on to the kitchen floor. She thought of how he had accepted their hurried, trite explanations as to why he must never enter the café itself, and the one occasion when he had and was met by a multitude of startled, staring eyes, how he had beguilingly explained that it must have been because his apron was dirty. She thought of all these things and felt her heart turn to granite and heard her voice, like a needle of bevelled glass.

'I don't want to keep him,' she said.

Chapter Ten

Anthony had been the name of the mongol in the café: it was never abbreviated or turned into a nickname. There were various theories about the whys and wherefores of his condition. The most usual was that his mother had been out driving while pregnant with him and had run out of petrol. She had pushed the car to the nearest petrol station – some considerable distance, so the story went – and the exertion of this had somehow taken its toll on the unborn child, and Anthony was the result. Other stories persisted, more vague and improbable, about curses from gypsy women selling clothes pegs, or how his mother had been given too much gas at his birth, or inherited imbecility from past generations. These stories and others would be muttered in hushed undertones whenever Anthony passed by with his mother.

Judith met his mother several times when she came to collect him from the café. She was a stout, cheerful woman in her late middle age, with a large bosom and large, grateful eyes. She always came by the back entrance and left by the same route. She would hold out Anthony's coat and ask him about his day and he would jabber excitedly at her, the way he did, and she would take his hand and thank everyone for being so kind to him and lead him out.

When Anthony was eighteen he started to hang around on the street corner outside his home, calling out to girls as they passed. Occasionally, but not as often as people thought, he would follow them up the street, always at a distance, stumbling along, eyes to the ground, talking to himself, and the girls would speed up their pace until they were rid of him. After a while he dropped out of sight and everyone forgot about him. His mother was still seen, hurrying along, a little older, a little fatter, but otherwise unchanged, flashing a smile at anyone who cared to enquire about him, her large eyes still grateful but veiled now and more knowing. 'He's in good hands,' she said, 'specialised hands which will help him fulfil his potential,' and she would hurry on, thanking them for their concern.

She managed a small, run down off-licence in the high street, which dealt in cut-price wine and cigarettes. It seemed there had once been a husband but when Anthony was six years old he left home. He didn't, apparently, leave for another woman and a cloud of accusation hung over his departure, though apparently he always swore it wasn't because of Anthony, of whom, he said, he was inordinately fond. Nevertheless, he never took up his access rights to visit his son: there was much speculation about this too for a time, but not for long; the stories about Anthony himself, about his fits of rage and incontinency, and the trial he must be to his poor mother were of more pressing interest. But even they eventually dried up. She copes marvellously, everyone said, heads wagging in sympathy, she must be superhuman; and they'd remind themselves to tell her so when they next visited the off-licence, but things being what they were they never quite got round to it.

Cynthia used to call in at the off-licence occasionally. It was in the next street. She used to complain that the wine was too warm, or the cigarettes stale from having sat on the shelf too long, but it was convenient and cheap. Sometimes Judith, as a child, had called in with her. She would hear Cynthia ask about Anthony, and the woman's hasty, cheerful replies, but it wasn't until she worked in the café that she actually came to meet him. She never once saw him in the off-licence, although she knew they lived right above it. She simply assumed he must be away or at school. There was often the sound of a television blaring out at full volume from upstairs, and sometimes footsteps heavily creaking across the ceiling above them, but that too was easily explained and she never troubled to dwell on it. Once, after they'd left the shop, she was skipping along when Cynthia said, 'Now there's a woman for you, she doesn't have to invent problems or unhappiness, she's got them right there, on the doorstep. It makes me feel ashamed.' Judith wondered what the words meant, and about the depth of her mother's feelings when she said them, but got distracted into eating her crisps and somehow never asked for an explanation.

* * *

After she had said she didn't want to keep the baby, Judith remembered her mother's words, and waited to feel ashamed herself. When the feeling failed to come she told herself it would probably come later, and she would find a way of coping with it then.

The paediatrician did not speak immediately and when he did, it was to say that Patrick had said the same thing, more or less, but that he had to hear it from Judith's own lips, unprompted, which is why he hadn't wanted her to look at her husband. Although she was relieved to hear that Patrick had echoed her feelings, Judith still did not look at him. She knew, instinctively and without a trace of doubt, that if she did she would see shame reflected in his eyes, and worse still, that he might see she felt none. Instead they sat, cowed and silent, while the paediatrician continued speaking. He told them, in a gentle, measured almost scholarly tone, that it was his job to act in the best interest of the baby. The baby had no voice, he said, whereas they did: his need was therefore greater. He told them their initial response was quite natural, but that there was no doubt that the baby, like any baby, would benefit from being within a warm, loving, family atmosphere: this had been proved countless times, he said. He told them of a case he'd read about where a mongol from such a family environment had actually got a place in a grammar school. Then he amended the statement like a calculated afterthought, conceding that this was probably rather an exceptional example. He said they might regard it as a tragedy, but Down's syndrome babies could grow into affectionate, responsive children, which many people felt compensated for their lack of potential.

As he spoke, Judith looked at her locker, at the familiar nestle of flowers and telegrams and fruit juice, and she wondered how they could remain so unaltered in the face of her devastation. After a while the paediatrician too fell silent. Beyond the wall of curtains they could hear the ward doors opening and closing behind the outgoing visitors, and, further away, the sound of tea cups rattling on a trolley. Listening to these sounds, Judith felt her scattered thoughts gather and mould and take shape. The fist inside her clenched itself once more. She pushed herself up in the bed, aware that the paediatrician was watching her, waiting for her to speak again.

'I'd like him removed from the end of the bed.'

Chapter Ten

'May I ask why?'

She almost laughed aloud, at the absurdity of the question, but a sudden caution prevented her. She must be cunning, or she'd be discovered. No one must ever know, ever, that she had felt nothing for the baby even before she knew about its condition; that she had felt nothing since that moment in the delivery room when the doctor had pronounced him a boy. That must be her secret, even from Patrick. The knowledge of this made her feel acutely alone, yet curiously undeterred. She felt no great apprehension at this, for she saw now that she had always been alone. She had allowed the intervention of Patrick in her life to be a welcome, but self-deluding, respite from that state. The revelation did not startle her. She accepted it with a dreary, flat objectivity, as if it were not herself she was reflecting upon but someone else. Equally she recognised that she would have to marshall all her resources, for she saw it was not the survival of the baby which was at stake, but her own.

'Any decision we make,' she said at length, 'should be made rationally. It mustn't be clouded by sentiment, which it will be if he remains here, where I can see him.'

She felt Patrick turn and stare at her as she said it. She heard herself saying the words but felt it was another person uttering them. She was two people now, one bruised and limp with shock, choking with unshed tears, the other artful and ruthless and full of resolve. In that second she realised, disquietingly, that she was, after all, her mother's daughter.

'Is it all right if I ring for a nurse?'

'As you wish.'

The paediatrician sounded disheartened. She found the switch and pressed it. Patrick cleared his throat and started asking questions about how and why such a thing could happen. They spoke of chromosomes and cells dividing imperfectly and genetic statistics, but Judith did not listen. Her concentration was centred only on the ward door opening, and the sound of a nurse's approaching footsteps. Only when they finally came, and she saw the curtains parting, did she turn back to the paediatrician, who promptly addressed her.

'You're sure this is what you want?'

'Quite sure.'

He looked away from her to the nurse. It was the one in the red striped uniform.

'Keep the baby in the nursery, will you? For the time being.'

The nurse nodded and a small, soundless tussle took place as she manoeuvred the trolley backwards out of the curtains. Judith kept her eyes on the paediatrician's face. She felt herself reach out for Patrick's hand and clutch it. She knew she should say something and protest as the curtains closed behind the baby. But she sat, eyes averted and silent.

After the baby had gone the paediatrician's manner altered somewhat. He became brisk and interrogative, but his quiet, considered tone remained, camouflaging both the questions and his response to them.

'I'd like to ask you a question, Mrs Fielding.'

'Yes?'

His attention, she noted, was directed at her rather than Patrick, as if he sensed she was the instrument of the resolve they shared.

'Why did you decide to have a child?'

'For much the same reason as anyone, I imagine.'

'Which is?'

She contemplated him silently, thinking that the question sounded like a test, and that she had never been good at tests. But that was in the past, when she had never sufficiently cared about the outcome.

'I suppose I wanted something . . . someone, who was part of us. Of Patrick and myself.'

'Which is what you have, in a way.'

'I have a child who will never grow up. I didn't want that.'

'Did you ever think about it before? While you were pregnant?'

'No.'

'Most women do.'

'Clearly I'm not like most women then.'

She spoke with complete candour. It had never occurred to her that anything would go wrong with the baby. She had once sat in the ante-natal clinic surrounded by a sea of swollen-bellied women and had privately speculated on how many of them would come to term and have normal healthy babies. It was not an equation she had ever applied to herself. She marvelled at the totality of that sense of immunity, lost now for ever. The paediatrician had risen to lean against the window, his arms implacably folded.

'Supposing I were to say to you that you might never have another child. Just as a hypothesis. What would you say?'

'I'd say the same thing.'

He shifted his eyes to Patrick.

'And you?'

'Yes.'

'Why do you say you're not like most women?'

He was looking at her again.

'I suppose because most women don't have this happening to them, do they?'

'How do you think they'd react if they did?'

'I've no idea.'

'I'm not criticising you, Mrs Fielding. I just want to be sure you're aware of what you're saying, and why.'

'I understand.'

'I hope so.'

He said it simply, almost carelessly.

'Are there any questions you want to ask me?'

She paused in thought before replying.

'Explain it to me again, please. Why? I'm only twenty-five. I'm young. I thought it only happened to older women.'

There was an undisguised plaintiveness in her voice, as a new and mounting sense of injustice took hold.

'That is more usually the case, but not always. To put it at its simplest, it shows a genetic predisposition. There are two types. One we call genetic, which means that one of the parents carries an imperfect chromosome in their cellular make-up, which can reveal itself when they produce a Down's syndrome child. The other is more common. We call it sporadic. It's where the chromosome count in both parents is completely normal, but at the point of conception, when the ovum and the sperm fuse and the cell divides, there is one extra chromosome present. It's a chance phenomenon which increases with age.'

Judith stared at him struggling to understand. But she did not entirely understand. She saw only that the baby was the result of some unseen flaw in Patrick or herself, like a timber buried within the structure of a house, tainted and rotting with some invisible pestilence which spreads until eventually the whole edifice decays and crumbles. She and Patrick turned to look at one another, in mute and urgent consternation. Even the touch of the other's hand seemed now like an accusation.

'It's unlikely, very, that you're the former type, the genetic type. Statistically it's much rarer. The chances are your chromosome counts are both completely normal.'

The paediatrician, as if perceiving the electric tension pass between them, spoke quickly.

'It's much more likely that you're the sporadic type.

There might be a slight genetic predisposition but it's just bad luck you happened to hit it. Anyway, a test on the baby's blood will determine it within ten days.'

Judith felt Patrick grip her hand.

'And if we're the genetic sort?' she asked. 'If it is something in one of us?'

'As I said, I doubt very much that's the case.'

'But it's not impossible.'

'No,' he conceded, his reluctance evident.

'And if we are, what then?'

'It's down to what's called genetic ratios, Mrs Fielding. A sample of blood from you both is analysed, and the genetic likelihood of it recurring is calculated.'

'What could that likelihood be?'

'You're really being very bleak about it, Mrs Fielding. In all probability . . . '

She gestured impatiently, surprised at herself. It was she who was now the interrogator.

'I simply want to know the chances of it happening again.'

'That can vary enormously.'

'For example?'

He hesitated a second.

'They can range, say, from anything between one in ten or upwards. It's really impossible to assess, just like that.'

'But we could carry a one in ten chance of it happening again, if not more?'

A moment passed, before he nodded. Her mind darted this way and that. Patrick's fingers were pressing into her palm. She was speaking for them both now, and for that part of herself still too numb and bereft to rally.

'And if they're as high as that?'

'It's really most unlikely.'

'What's happened already is unlikely. Since, as you

71

say, we're dealing in likelihoods, we may as well know them all.'

Patrick was gazing at her again, astonished at the compassionless purpose behind her inquisition.

'Very well. If the genetic ratio is that high . . . high enough to make it probable the same thing might happen . . . you would be advised to think very seriously whether you should have another child.'

Chapter Eleven

The paediatrician stayed with them over an hour. Judith sat straight-backed in the bed, tirelessly questioning and probing, as if trying to find the answer to a riddle which eluded her as soon as she thought she'd grasped it. Patrick too asked questions, but less diligently, less intently than she. He sat hunched beside her as she navigated them forward. He was full of admiration for her composure and her strength, and a little frightened by it. He was not angered by what was happening to him, but chastened and terribly sad. He had seen the baby only at a few snatched moments, and believed, when he did, that he was already starting to love it; only a vague, hesitant kind of feeling, for he had not had the opportunity for it to grow into anything else, but now that the baby was absent he felt an almost intolerable sense of loss, which puzzled him. His feelings were less complex than those of Judith, he knew this, but then he was less used to dealing with such things. He had long since accepted this imbalance between them. He blamed himself for what had occurred, or at least he told himself that he should, out of a sense of fair play. After all, he had congratulated himself at the speed with which he had got her pregnant, it seemed only right that he should shoulder the responsibility now events had turned against them. He wondered what his parents would say when he told them, and how he would tell them. He felt older than he had in years.

He tried not to think of the baby in the nursery, because that, too, frightened him. Unlike Judith, he had never known a mongol at first hand, but he had always felt frightened of them, even when he caught a glimpse of them in the street; he never knew why they alarmed him so, and he didn't stop to ask why now. He simply felt sad that his son would evoke the same response in others. He was sad too that there was a possibility they might not be able to have a normal child, although his common sense told him that the paediatrician was probably right about this being unlikely. He considered their lives as a childless couple, and decided they would simply have to make a virtue of it. They would be able to travel unencumbered and pursue a more active social life and take up interests that people with children could not afford or were prevented from doing. He knew these to be trivial advantages, but clung to them in an effort to be positive. He wished he had worn his other jacket, because there were still two Valium wrapped in tin foil in the breast pocket.

Before he left them, the paediatrician told them that his diagnosis would be officially confirmed when the results of the blood test on the baby were known. He said he was so confident in his assessment of their son's condition that he had decided to tell them straight away. To have done anything else, he said, would have been hypocrisy. He told them again that in his view the baby's place was with them, rather than in institutional care, and that he hoped they would come round to agreeing with him. He said this gently, without any hint of condescension. He said he would visit Judith again the next day, and that she could call him in the meantime, night or day, and he would come to her. Then he left them.

After he'd gone, Patrick and Judith clung together with an unfamiliar desperation, and Patrick lay his head in her lap while she stroked his hair. He said she'd taken it marvellously, and she replied she was probably in a state of shock. The visiting hour was well over by now and they began to wonder how much longer Patrick would be allowed to remain. Then Judith suddenly remembered the raisin-eyed midwife and the attempts at breast feeding and was charged with a new and simmering anger. She felt, knowing it to be unreasonable but feeling it nonetheless, that she had been maliciously conspired against by the nurses. She allowed herself to feel this unreservedly, for she knew that her sense of outrage would carry her through the next steps which had to be taken. The most immediate step was to get away from the babies and mothers around her. Whereas she had once relied on these mothers for wisdom and support, she knew she would now find any platitudes and sympathy suffocating; she knew that neither would help her. She recognised, of course, that the women were not conspiring against her but she regarded the presence of their babies to be an unintentional conspiracy, and because of that, a threat.

There was a sister on duty at the nurses' station in the corridor outside the ward. She was in her late thirties, with an unlined, unmade-up face and a thatch of thick brown hair. Expressionlessly, she watched Judith and Patrick approach. Judith was wearing her new dressing gown, white with pink gingham checks and ruffles on the sleeves and collar. She had bought it the week before her confinement; it had seemed then to make her look young and pretty, but now she felt the ruffles made her look faintly absurd. Patrick held her under one arm as she walked, for the pain between her legs was worse when she was upright. When they reached the nurses' station they paused, and the sister rested her eyes, grey and impassive, on Judith.

'What can I do for you?'

'I'm Mrs Fielding.'

'Yes?'

'I'd like to get out of the main ward. Into a side room. I'm sure you understand why.'

The sister glanced at Patrick, her brows raised enquiringly.

'I think it'll be less distressing for my wife,' he said, 'in the circumstances,' he added.

'I'll see what I can do.'

They expected her to move away, to ask or check with someone, but instead she simply consulted a list on the desk in front of her.

'I'm sorry, we don't have one available.'

'But we saw one back there, empty.'

'A mother is coming up from the labour ward now. It's allocated to her.'

'Is it private? I mean, if it's a question of money . . . '

Patrick's voice faltered as the sister looked sharply at him.

'It's nothing to do with that, Mr Fielding.'

'Can't she have my bed?' Judith asked.

'I'm sorry, Mrs Fielding. In any case, I happen to think you're better off in the ward with the other mothers.'

'Why?'

'I don't think it's good for you to be shut away on your own.'

'I'm not alone. My husband is with me.'

'Not all the time he won't be, will he?'

'Yes, as a matter of fact.'

The sister seemed to fix her gaze on some point beyond Judith's left shoulder.

'I'm sorry, that simply isn't possible.'

'I see.'

Judith's hands clenched into balls inside the frilled pockets of her dressing gown.

'In that case I'm just going to have to discharge myself.'

Something stirred in the sister's face.

'Mrs Fielding . . . you've just had a baby . . . you can't possibly . . . '

'Give me a room of my own and let my husband stay with me or I'll discharge myself. Now.'

The sister stared at her in open, silent inspection.

'Wait a minute.'

She disappeared behind a door, her feet whispering on the polished tiled floor.

'Will you really discharge yourself?'

'You think I'm bluffing?'

Patrick shook his head. He didn't quite know how to cope with her in this new frame of mind. The sister returned.

'You can have the room. If you wait there your things will be brought to you.'

'And my husband?'

'He can stay.'

'Thank you.'

As they turned away from her, Judith, unobserved by anyone, smiled in satisfaction. She knew the triumph to be petulant, but regarded it as a triumph all the same.

The side ward was one of two opposite the ward Judith had just vacated. As she and Patrick made their way up the corridor towards it, the door of the adjacent room was suddenly flung open and the woman in the orange dressing gown emerged. Judith felt her stomach lurch at the sight of her. The woman was standing quite motionless in the corridor. Other mothers limped past her, holding air cushions and pushing baby trolleys, and she smiled toothlessly at each of them, as she fingered the buttons on her dressing gown. As Judith drew close, she turned, one eye rolling wildly towards Patrick, so that she appeared to look at them both simultaneously.

'I keep missing it.'

'I'm sorry?'

'The tea trolley. I keep missing it. They forget about you in there.'

Judith nodded politely, to acknowledge that she'd heard, and quickly steered Patrick towards her side ward. The woman stood, fidgeting with her buttons, watching them.

'We'll be neighbours then. That's nice.'

She said something else, but Judith didn't wait to hear it. She closed the door on the woman and leant against it, her heart pounding. For a second she felt the dry twig of fear tapping inside her head once more, and the hard core of her resolve slacken. She saw Patrick's face, white with concern, bending over her.

'Are you all right?'

'Yes, yes. It's that woman. She disturbs me.'

'She looks harmless enough. You can't let things get to you now.'

'I won't.'

She smiled at him, and touched his face. He looked as she imagined he must have sometimes looked as a child, injured and a little baffled. They moved to the bed, pristine and freshly made, and sat on it in companionable solitude, gazing at the window. It occurred to Judith they had not yet discussed either the baby or their decision. Presumably Patrick felt the same as she did, that there was nothing to discuss. But she could feel the decision like a presence in the room isolating and imprisoning them.

'We've got to tell everyone. My parents ... your mother.'

Patrick's voice was strained to disguise his apprehension.

'I know.'

She looked at her watch and was astonished to see that only an hour and ten minutes had elapsed since the paediatrician had left them. She felt as if a lifetime of experience had been compacted into that time dividing her, like a wall, from the events preceding it, but through its chinks still allowing her faint glimpses of the familiar landscape of her past. She knew she was being compelled forward, out of the years of careful prudency, towards some foreign and dangerous destination. She wondered, seated beside Patrick in that tiled and white-washed room, how it was that someone who had just given birth to, and rejected, a mentally retarded child, did not feel any sense of guilt or failure, but should feel instead only the perfect simplicity of her own self.

* * *

They phoned Cynthia first. Judith plugged the coinbox telephone into a socket outside the side ward and wheeled the machine inside while Patrick went to ask a nurse for some change. It was the sister who gave it to him, counting it out on the desk between them. When she'd finished she asked if he would like to look in on the baby.

'No, no. I don't think so. Thank you, but no.'

He scraped up the money and strode quickly, conscious of her eyes on his back and the reproach of her thoughts.

Cynthia was in the bath when Judith rang. She was tempted to let the phone ring unanswered, but knew that it was not in her nature. She stood dripping by the telephone, listening to the pips.

'Mother?'

'Judith. I was just in the bath.'

'I'm sorry.'

The water was gathering in dark, liquid pools around her feet. Judith's voice sounded thin and distant. She continued speaking a moment, and as Cynthia listened, she stared down at the water, trickling from her toes on to the carpet. She imagined herself back in the bath, nodding to sleep, her glass of gin cupped in her hands over her chest. She imagined the sound of the telephone ringing and her temptation not to answer it. She saw herself climbing out of the bath and moving to the phone and hearing the sound of the pips and her daughter's dead voice, saying the words. What she was hearing and the experience of hearing it fused in her mind into a brutal understanding.

'Oh my God, are you sure?'

'Yes.'

'Perhaps they've made a mistake. You know what these doctors are like.'

'There's no mistake, Mother.'

The spark of hope flickered and died.

'Do you want me to come in and see you?'

'No, Patrick's here. I'm all right. I'm coping.'

'Oh God, what a thing. I can't take it in.'

'No.'

She thought of her daughter as she'd last seen her, in her hospital bed, plump and soft and full of pride, and ached at the memory. Judith was speaking again.

'Anyway, we've decided not to keep him. I thought you should know.'

'Not keep him?'

'Yes.'

'Are you . . . Can you do that?'

'Do what?'

A thread of alarm had entered Judith's voice.

'He's your son. Are you allowed to just . . . ?'

'I don't care what we're allowed to do. I don't want to keep him.'

'I just meant . . . legally. The legality of it.'

'I'm not going to make a martyr of myself because of a . . . a genetic accident.'

The words were shrill with defiance. Cynthia felt herself slump into submission.

'No. I simply meant . . . you must do what you think is best, of course.'

'I hope for your support in this, Mother.'

There was a note of authority in Judith's voice she did not recognise.

'Of course. Of course.'

'Find out the legalities then. You're always saying you've got contacts. Find out just what the legal situation is.'

'I'll try.'

'I'll call you again in a couple of hours.'

The phone clicked. Cynthia moved back to the bathroom. She pulled out the plug and perched, naked, on the side of the bath. There was a trail of wet footprints on the carpet leading to the telephone in the bedroom. She sat shivering, thinking of the baby, struggling to recollect his face, and failing. Her hands were turning blue. She snatched up her gin and hurried back to the bedroom, where she climbed into bed, the glass rattling against her teeth. She picked up her address book and skimmed over the names and numbers, but the letters danced in front of her eyes. She looked away, back to the carpet, where the damp impression of her feet still remained. When they were dry she would start making telephone calls. By then she would be in charge of herself once again; she would have devised some plan to help her daughter.

* * *

Chapter Eleven

Patrick's father was out when he telephoned. He generally took a walk at the end of the day, calling in at the local pub for a beer and a chat with the publican, who shared his passion for cricket. It was Patrick's mother who answered the telephone. She listened dry-eyed as Patrick haltingly told her about the baby. She had always connected mongols with German measles, but when she said this he irritably told her it had nothing to do with it. It was all to do with chromosomes. She did not know what a chromosome was, but did not like to ask. She felt slow and stupid and shared his irritation with her.

When they had finished speaking she went into the garden. It had rained that afternoon and there was a snail on the back porch. They often appeared after a rainfall and this irritated her too. As she watched it slowly pull itself across the stone flags, she wept at the unfairness of it, that her grandchild should be so afflicted. She wondered what she would tell her husband and how he would react. She knew he would say it didn't come from their side of the family, because he was given to saying such things. She knew, also, that he would be relieved they had decided not to keep the baby, because he could then dismiss it from his mind; he had that ability which he often said she lacked. The snail had now reached the edge of the porch and was heading for one of the geranium pots under the kitchen window. She walked over to it and, still weeping, stepped on it. She had to put all her weight on it, grinding it, before she felt it crunch and then squash under her shoe. Then she took her shoe off and carried it over to the garden tap, where she rinsed the remains of shell and flesh from the sole. She was still weeping. She heard the front door thud and stooped quickly to replace the shoe. She wished she knew more about chromosomes so that she could explain more fully what Patrick had told her. Thinking this, she wiped her eyes and re-entered the house.

*   *   *

Chris was out when they telephoned, which somehow seemed typical. They had hoped he would be able to tell them something of the legal situation; they knew there were other people to call, but Patrick had left the address book at home. They were disappointed: while they had been telephoning, another hour had passed and they were anxious that time should pass quickly. A nurse brought Judith a yellow pill, which Patrick recognised as Valium; they discussed whether or not they should break it in half but Patrick pointed out it might crumble and they would lose most of it in the process. He looked at it hungrily and Judith gave it to him quite readily. She had persuaded herself anyway that she didn't want it.

Most of the time they held hands, Patrick sometimes raising her fingers to his lips and kissing them, but absently, his eyes cast down. Twice Judith had to leave the sanctuary of the room to go to the lavatory and replace her sanitary towel. On both occasions Patrick accompanied her, hovering conspicuously outside the lavatory. Neither of them wanted to be alone. Supper was served inside the room, Patrick's delivered later than Judith's, when the heated trolley had done the full rounds of the wards, for it was explained he could only have what was left over. The business of eating seemed a trifling intrusion and they were surprised to find they were so hungry. At nine o'clock Judith telephoned her mother again.

'Well, did you find out?'

'Yes. I rang an old friend. A solicitor.'

'And?'

'He said it's a little outside his sphere, but yes, you're basically within your rights not to keep him.'

Judith felt her tension dissolve into relief.

'Did he say anything else?'

'How sorry he was. That sort of thing.'

'I mean about what we should do.'

'He said ... ' There was a crackle on the line and Cynthia's voice faded.

'Mother?'

'I'm still here.'

'What else did he say?'

'He said not to take the baby home. Something about strands of care. You have to leave the baby in the hospital. Abandon it. Those were the words he used.'

'Is that it?'

'More or less.'

'Is that what he advised me to do?'

'Not really.'

Cynthia sounded guarded now.

'His brother's got a mongol. He said he was very fond of him.'

'I see.'

Judith's tone was dry and unpleasant.

'You're bound to get that sort of thing.'

'Of course. I don't mind.'

'You'd be inhuman if you didn't. You can't just shut things out, Judith.'

'I don't want to talk about it now, please.'

Patrick was by the window, watching her, his expression fixed.

'Is there anything else he said?'

'No. He said the legal situation was pretty clear, but it was doubtful anyone would tell you that. Keeping these children is expensive, both for you and the state. Everyone will try and avoid it if they can.'

'So it all comes down to economics?'

'In that respect, I suppose, yes.'

The pips went and Judith pushed more money in the box.

'Look, there's something I want to say,' Cynthia said,

as soon as they were connected again. Judith gritted her teeth.

'I want to help you. However I can. I mean, I know they can be a handful, children like Jack . . . but I'm sure I could help you. I could get a flat nearby and come in every day. It's worth a try, isn't it?'

It was the first time he had been called by his chosen name. Judith remembered the balcony overlooking the mountains, the scattering of lights in the dark valley, the ice tinkling in her glass as they giggled over names.

'What I mean is,' Cynthia was saying, 'will you think about it, at least?'

'No. This is one thing I don't have to think about. Besides you'd be no better at it than me.'

'No, well, I just wanted to help.'

She sounded disappointed but undiscouraged. Judith felt a stab of apprehension, but swiftly discounted it. She knew the legal situation. She was protected and the decision was protected. Nothing could jeopardise that now.

Chapter Twelve

After her second telephone conversation with Judith, Cynthia sat once again in the wicker chair on her verandah. She was filled with painful resentment after Judith's brusque rejection of her offers to help and, to distract herself, had turned her mind to the past. She saw that all her relationships had somehow glanced off her, temporarily bruising her perhaps, but otherwise leaving her intact. In the past she had always been rather proud of this fact, but now she was assailed by a sudden doubt.

Chapter Twelve

The ranks of faces of those people who had once been such a source of compelling emotion to her now moved silently through her mind. She could barely remember most of their names. Were they as unaltered by the relationship they had once shared as she was? She thought of her two husbands, and then of Judith, and decided probably not. This thought made her uneasy, knowing it was too late to make amends.

It was at this point that the confusion in her mind clarified itself into something like an inspiration. There might after all be an opportunity to make amends.

*   *   *

The bed was too narrow for them both to sleep in and it was decided that Patrick should sleep on the chair, which he did, his head resting on Judith's chest. They lay that way for some time, occasionally asking each other how they felt, anxious to monitor the other's emotional progress. Patrick could hear the beat of Judith's heart and was surprised at its steadiness. He was no longer frightened of her strength, but grateful for it. He tilted his chin up to her and she inclined her head, allowing him to brush her throat with his lips. Her neck felt soft and warm. They must, he told himself, have other children, normal children, whatever the risks. They would put this event behind them and perhaps, in time, be enriched by it. He wanted to tell her this, but somehow the words wouldn't connect. He was afraid she might think him simplistic. She was, he observed, despite all the paediatrician's assurances, determined to be pessimistic. Yet he knew that it was out of her hopelessness that his own hope now sprang. That, too, made him grateful.

He marvelled at the courage with which she could face so many hidden implications, and felt a little envious. He wondered if there was a biological explanation for her new resolve and strength of mind. Some kind of post-natal hormonal disturbance perhaps, which had coincided with the events of the previous day to carry her through. Or carry them both through, for he was not slow to appreciate that Judith's timely decisiveness had been beneficial to him also. Then he chided himself. It was an insulting assumption. She had responded as magnificently as she had because she had the resources to do so – resources of which he'd been largely unaware, perhaps, but that in no way invalidated them. He must regard it as an unexpected bonus. Things would anyway settle down in the next few days. When she had got over the shock she would inevitably feel depressed and vulnerable and she would probably cry and it would be his turn to be supportive. By then he too would be back to his old self. He felt reassured, and concentrated his attention on getting some sleep.

Judith also slept, but long after Patrick. She lay, feeling the weight of his head, listening to the regular, familiar sound of his breathing. She heard other sounds too. The babies were crying in the nursery again. She listened to them, trying to force herself to be detached from them. She tried to think of them as just anonymous sounds, like the drone of the traffic from the street beneath, or the hum of the hospital generator. But they had a cogency the other sounds lacked which tugged at her consciousness, pulling her attention back to them.

She heard another sound then, closer by. The sound of a chair scraping and a voice coughing. It was the woman in the adjoining side ward. The sound of this also disturbed her and she stirred restlessly, causing Patrick to raise his head and murmur. Quickly she caressed him and he lowered his head. Her thoughts returned to the woman in the next door room. It struck her they were two outcasts, forced into exile from the other mothers: the only difference being that her exile was voluntary. She thought of the woman's baby in the special unit, surrounded by the vibrating life-support systems. She thought of its dead brain and wondered if intelligence could be rated by electronic impulses, and, if so, would the meagre brain of her own baby register in the same way? Her thoughts were fragmented and painful and her head ached with the pain of containing them. Finally, she slept. Her dreams too were fragmented. At one point she saw a lavatory, chipped and stained with urine, and protruding from it the gently inflating crown of her baby's head. She saw her hand, with the hospital bracelet around its wrist, reach in and pull him out a few inches to check his genitalia, and then the same hand carefully replacing him. It was only one of many dreams she had that night, and while the memory of it evaded her on waking the following morning, the feeling of it persisted.

* * *

She was discharged the next morning. In the event she didn't have to discharge herself, although she announced her intention to do so. The ward sister, her mouth compressed in silent disapproval, rang for the paediatrician and in turn the doctor who had delivered her, and who was officially responsible for her discharge. Patrick and Judith awaited their arrival in the side ward. As they waited, there was a light tap on the door and the ward sister entered. Her movements were quick and soundless. Her look of disapproval had now given way to one of guarded tolerance. She sat down on the chair in front of them, her grey eyes intently fastened on their faces.

'It would really be much better for you to stay a little longer.'

She was addressing Judith, but appealing to Patrick.

'Not just physically, but to recuperate generally. You've been through a lot, God knows you have. You're bound to feel . . .' she hesitated, searching for the word, 'confused. It's only natural. Give yourself a few days to adjust. To come to terms. You might feel quite differently if you do.'

'You mean, I might change my mind about keeping him?'

Judith's voice was hard with antagonism.

'It's possible. I've seen it happen before.'

'All the more reason to go now, I'd have thought.'

'Mrs Fielding . . . '

'You're wasting your breath. You can't say anything I haven't said to myself.'

'Mrs Fielding, please . . . just go and see him. You don't have to go into the nursery. Just look through the window. Give yourself that chance, please.'

'No.'

'Why not?'

'I don't want to.'

'But why not? What are you frightened of?'

Judith clamped her mouth obstinately shut. She saw a wave of contempt pass over the sister's face.

'I don't understand women like you. I'll never understand women like you. He needs you. He's a lovely baby, in spite of everything. As bonny as they come.'

'Oh God, do I really have to listen to this?'

'You were happy enough to try and feed him, weren't you? Before you knew there was something wrong with him.'

'He hasn't got a bloody cold, you know. He isn't going to get better!' Judith was astounded at her hostility. 'You think he's so lovely, you have him. As a gift. Take him. I'll sign anything you want. He's yours.'

'That kind of talk helps no one.'

'You see, you don't want him either, do you? Why is it so different for me? Because I had the bad luck to have him? You just want me to do what you think is right so it's all nice and neat with no loose ends . . . '

Chapter Twelve

She was shouting now. Patrick laid a hand on her arm.

'She's only trying to do her job, Judith.'

'She doesn't have to try so bloody hard, does she?'

With a grimace of hopelessness, the sister rose.

'A lot of people wouldn't consider it bad luck, Mrs Fielding. They'd consider it a privilege to have such a child.'

She swung past them, out of the room. They sat without speaking. Judith felt an anger so intense she wouldn't have thought it possible. She reached for Patrick's hand and caught sight of his eyes, anxious and perplexed, resting on hers, and that too made her angry, though she didn't know why.

'She thinks I'm unnatural. Everyone does.'

'Nonsense.' He smiled at her quickly, in reassurance, his forefinger brushing her cheek. 'Anyway, I'd like to see them have the courage to make such a difficult decision.'

'It isn't difficult,' she said bluntly, 'it's easy. That's the trouble.'

His smile faded, the finger on her cheek dropped away. They continued to wait in silence.

The paediatrician when he came was compliant and patient. He too wanted her to re-think her decision, but her rebuttals were so firm that he didn't mention it again. He had seen the baby that morning, he said. He seemed healthy enough and the nurses were taking good care of him. Judith simply smiled politely. He talked to Patrick about genetic counselling and whom they should contact when the results of the baby's blood tests were known. When they were finished he glanced at Judith and enquired if she understood all his explanations from the previous day. She answered with a nod and he said:

'Did you smoke at all in your pregnancy?'

'No.'

'I was going to say, if you had, it's got nothing to do with that, you mustn't blame yourself.'

'Thank you, but it doesn't apply.'

She smiled at him for the first time, in a mixture of irony and sadness, and he smiled back, his face wearing the same expression.

Ten minutes later Judith, now in her own clothes, was walking down the corridor with Patrick. A small knot of nurses stood gathered at the nurses' station, watching them go. Judith and Patrick looked neither to right nor left, keeping their eyes fixed on the lift at the end of the passage. They walked past the gravely watching nurses and the sister's office and the glass window of the baby nursery and the ward kitchen and sluice room, until they reached the waiting lift. Once inside it, and against their better judgement, they turned to look quickly back up the corridor. The nurses were no longer standing, but scattering, their attention already diverted. There was the faint sound of babies crying from the nursery, the faint cloying odour of breast milk in the air, and, as the lift doors closed, the distant, lilting sound of a voice singing 'Save all your kisses for me'.

Chapter Thirteen

When they got home there was a pile of letters to answer. Judith sat on a cushion in the sitting room, writing them, while Patrick went shopping. 'We're coping,' she wrote, 'you needn't worry about us.' She repeated the same words in every letter; she explained the decision in one line. 'I hope you won't judge us too harshly, no one can know how they'd respond in such a situation unless it happens to them.' Re-reading it, she was pleased with the wording; it had just the right blend of authority and humility.

Patrick returned later with fish and chips and they ate it out of the paper off the kitchen table. The house was quiet, like the street outside; people were still at work. They felt like children playing truant.

Later in the afternoon a midwife called round. She was ageing and Irish with decorated spectacles. She sat beside Judith on the bed, packing away her blood pressure equipment, clucking her tongue in undisguised sympathy.

'It's so sad,' she said. 'So sad, and the first baby too.'

The absence of the baby should have made her presence intrusive, yet it didn't. She examined Judith's stitches admiringly, and told her she was a fine strong girl, there would be other babies. Judith did not find this remark as irritating as she had anticipated. It was direct and simple and contrasted satisfyingly with her mood. They went downstairs, where Patrick had prepared tea. They drank it in the kitchen, the midwife standing, leaning against the door, the teacup in her gloved hands. She knew of another like theirs she said, in a street nearby, she had delivered it herself; and she clucked her tongue at the memory.

'How could you tell?' Judith asked curiously.

'Oh, you get to know what to look for with these things. The eyes, the muscle tone, the way the hands are formed ... '

Judith thought of the labour ward, of the sudden, hurried evacuation of the nurses and doctors after her delivery.

'Did they keep him?'

'Oh yes. She was the youngest of five. It was less of a blow. And a large family, it can absorb these things better somehow.'

Judith glanced around at the stripped pine dresser and the gleaming, polished floor of her kitchen. The clock on the cooker was ticking; she was surprised she had never noticed it before.

The next visitor was Wanda, from next door. Wanda was exactly ten years older than Judith, and nearly six foot. She was bronzed and statuesque, married to a skin specialist, with three school-age children. She had seen the car, she said, and had popped in hoping to catch a glimpse of the baby. They told her about him together, unhurriedly and succinctly, pausing to allow the other to elaborate or qualify where necessary. Their roles divided neatly in the explanation, Patrick discussing the genetic aspect, the finer points on chromosomes and cell divisions, whereas Judith took on the voice of a narrator, saying who had told them and when, and why they had made the decision they had. They knew that it was a performance they would have to give again, and both made mental notes to omit or add a detail next time round.

Wanda stood listening, her hands on her wide, bony hips. She was wearing a sleeveless T-shirt and a pleated flowered skirt. Her legs were bare. She was forthright and practical in her response, as they knew she would be.

'You definitely did the right thing,' she said when they had finished. She did not waste energy on sympathy or idle remarks. She managed her conversations with the same capable efficiency as she did her home.

'Frank says they're a one hundred per cent genetic write-off, no two ways about it.' Frank was her husband. 'And you can have a test with any other pregnancy . . . they can test to make sure the baby's normal; if not they terminate, it's all very safe and straightforward.'

'Yes, the paediatrician said.'

'Thank God he told you when he did. They don't in some hospitals, you know. Particularly out in the sticks.

They let you take them home and find out in your own way. It's a bloody outrage.'

She paced restlessly between them. Her energy made them feel tired.

'You want my advice, get yourself a damn good lawyer ... give him power of attorney. Just hand the whole problem over and forget it. Forget the whole wretched thing. He can sign all the care orders, do all the arranging. That's certainly what I'd do in your position.'

Patrick and Judith exchanged a glance, their thoughts turning to Chris. Judith looked down at her hands arranged neatly on her lap. She could feel the blood draining out of her, and wondered if it was staining her skirt.

'I think we should see it through. All of it.'

She was aware of a look passing between Wanda and Patrick.

'I'm sorry, but I just think we should. I feel it very strongly. I can't explain why.'

'Fair enough. You must do whatever you want, of course.'

Wanda's mind was racing again.

'I'll cook and shop for you. I've some cold joint left, I'll rustle up a salad and bring it round. You make out a list of anything you want.' She paused, listening for the sound of her children returning from school. 'And tomorrow, come round to our place for dinner. We'll ask some other people. Make a night of it. About eight-thirty, give me a chance to get the kids to bed first.'

Judith imagined her on the telephone, arranging it. 'We've these neighbours ... such a sweet couple ... just had a mongol ... they're feeling a bit low, so I thought I'd cheer them up.'

Wanda's open face was looking down at her.

'Anything you want, anything at all, don't hesitate. And never regret what you've done, Judith. I mean, they're quick enough to abort up to twenty-eight weeks of pregnancy, aren't they? Yet a few weeks later they're going on about the sanctity of life. It makes me sick. If he was mine I'd leave him by an open window and let nature take its course.'

Her tone was vigorous and a little grim. She touched Judith on the shoulder.

'I'll see myself out.'

After she'd gone, Patrick sat on the sofa, chewing his nails. There was an expression on his face which Judith did not recognise. Then he looked at his watch and stood up.

'I think I'll just pop round to the doctor. I'll catch the surgery if I hurry.'

'What for?'

'I'm getting low on Valium. I'll get enough for you too. And some sleeping pills.'

'I need some of those other pills . . . that make your milk dry up . . . '

He paused a moment.

'Yes, yes of course.'

He snatched up the car keys and went out. She heard his footsteps sprinting down the front path, and the gate swing closed. Next door she could hear Wanda shouting at her children. 'I'm not a servant, you know. You treat this place like a hotel.' She leant back in the armchair. She remembered other afternoons in the chair, listening to Wanda's voice raised in reprimand to her children, feeling the baby kick inside her. Her hands felt empty suddenly, and unoccupied. She went upstairs and filled a bath, scattering a handful of salt into it as the midwife had instructed her. She got into the bath and watched the clouds of rust-coloured blood rise to the surface, her fingers exploring the wrinkled indentations from the stretch marks on her abdomen. Next week Patrick would be back at work. She would have not just afternoons but whole days to fill. Then she remembered the nursery. The cot would have to be dismantled and the baby clothes put away. Perhaps they should redecorate while they were at it, and make another spare room out of it. There would, after all, be demands on her time.

When Patrick arrived at the surgery it was packed. He squatted on a low bench in a corner and resigned himself to a long wait. Within seconds of sitting down, his heart started to pound uncomfortably. He was surrounded by babies. For a moment he began to wonder if he'd stumbled into a baby clinic, but then he realised that his first impression was inaccurate and exaggerated. In fact there were only three babies.

Calmer now, he glanced around at them. They were dotted about the room, each one reclining in the curve of its mother's arm. The nearest was only a foot or so away. It was dressed in yellow and brown stripes, giving it the appearance of a plump, bald bumble bee. Now that he came to study it, its face was oddly adult. It seemed to have a slightly bored, laconic expression. Eventually, as if aware of his gaze, it turned to look directly at him. He was seized by a sudden panic. Its eyes were wide and metallic blue and held his in a steady, devouring stare. It reminded him of a childhood game where one person stares fixedly at the other, and the first one to blink or look away is the loser. He stared into the baby's eyes, conscious of his heart pounding, his hands gripping his bent knees. Then the baby disconcerted him by suddenly smiling, its lips parting in a toothless, almost gormless grin. It was an idiotic smile, with no hint of idiocy about it. He laughed aloud at its expression and then quickly he left the room. He would have to telephone and ask for a prescription to be left for him. Outside he caught sight of a woman walking by, pushing a pram, and across the road at a bus stop, another woman with a pushchair. He felt for his car keys and hurried to his car.

*   *   *

Chris called round that evening, quite late. Patrick had already gone to bed. Judith was in the kitchen. She was turning out a cupboard, crouched in front of it, sorting through the contents, discarding some items into a rubbish bag, stacking others in neat piles. When Patrick had announced he was going to bed, she had felt too wakeful and agitated to accompany him. She had remembered the cupboard and her intention to give it a thorough clean-out as soon as she had the opportunity. It was full of domestic bits and pieces, balls of string and pinking shears and table mats and cutlery sets they had received as wedding presents, some still in their presentation boxes. She scoured the shelves with bleach, then rinsed them, and lined them with tin foil. She was still doing this when Chris rang the door bell.

He already knew what had happened; he had called in at the hospital at the end of the evening visiting session and a nurse had told him. He stood in the kitchen, amongst the rubbish bags and strips of tin foil, his face tense with embarrassment and compassion. She offered him coffee, and when she brushed past him to put the kettle on, he caught her arm and pulled her roughly towards him. He held her tightly, pressing her body against his, his head pushed into her neck, murmuring words of sympathy. She felt large and awkward in his arms, acutely conscious of her bulging abdomen and of Patrick, sedated with sleeping pills, above them. After a moment she disentangled herself and made the coffee. He looked at the disgorged cupboard and remarked that it was an odd time to choose to do the spring cleaning, and she found herself laughing. Later, they carried the coffee into the sitting room where she told him of Wanda's suggestion about getting a power of attorney, and her own reluctance to accede to it.

'It's certainly one way of handling it,' he said. 'What's your objection?'

'It seems . . . a little easy. I don't know. As if we're trying to sweep him under the carpet.'

'Don't you think you deserve things to be a little easy for a while?'

'No. Most people would say I've taken the easy way out already.'

'Utter nonsense.'

'You don't believe everyone will say that? Or think that?'

'What does it matter if they do?'

She stirred her coffee without looking at him.

'It doesn't. Perhaps it's simply what I feel myself.'

'What, that you've done the wrong thing you mean?'

He was frowning now, studing her carefully. She realised he was talking to her as she'd often heard him talk to Patrick; candidly, and in open friendship.

'Not at all,' she said in reply to his question. 'Oh, it's hopeless, I'll never explain it.'

'Try.'

'I feel . . . as though it was meant to happen. Oh, I know that it's just chance. Like a lottery, but I'm not the sort of person who wins things on lotteries.'

'That doesn't make sense.'

'I said it was hard to explain. But it happened to me, didn't it? Not to you or someone else, but to me. Why? There has to be some explanation. Some purpose in it.'

'You sound as though you want there to be.'

'Perhaps. A lot of people cling on to religion when something like this happens, don't they? Regard it as divine providence or whatever.'

She remembered the sister's words: Some people would consider it a privilege to have such a child.

'But I can't do that. I don't believe in God. I can't just conjure Him up now.'

'So you look for something else. It adds up to the same thing.'

'But there isn't anything else, is there? There's just the experience of it. And by saying what I have, I've tried to nullify it, to avoid it.'

'Well, if there is a point, perhaps that's it, experiencing what you are in rejecting him.'

She considered this a moment.

'In that case I have to see it through, don't I? All of it. I can't avoid that too.'

'Why, because you want to punish yourself?'

She seemed startled by this, and a little dismayed.

'Is that what you think?'

'It's one interpretation.'

She fell silent and he lit a cigarette.

'I don't know what's involved. I'm not that up-to-date on the Mental Health Act. It could be a little rough.'

She glanced at him sharply.

'Will there be a hearing?'

'I doubt it. But there are certain processes to go through. Technicalities mostly, but it still won't be easy. It's not intended to be.'

She made no comment. He watched her and said nothing for a moment. Then he said:

'Tell me, did the paediatrician say anything else about him? About his health? How strong he is?'

'Just that there wasn't any problem with him physically, not at the moment anyway.'

'What did you think when he said that?'

She reddened slightly before replying.

'I was disappointed.'

'Why?'

'I was hoping he would die.'

She said this quietly.

'Some of them do apparently,' Chris went on, apparently having decided to ignore her tone. 'I heard somewhere they've got dicky hearts. That they often need an operation to survive. I wondered if that applied to yours.'

'It seems not.'

'Pity.'

She flinched at his frankness and fixed her eyes on the plume of smoke from his cigarette, circling and drifting between them.

'I mean, if it turned out the child needed an operation . . . you could withhold permission, couldn't you? Then the whole thing is over and done with.'

'Assuming we decided to withhold permission.'

He looked at her steadily.

'Wishing him dead and . . . doing something about it aren't necessarily the same thing, are they?' She said it as a statement, but somehow it came out as a question. She was containing a mounting sense of distaste at the way the conversation was going, but knew she must continue with it. He considered her question in silence a second before tossing another back to her.

'What does Patrick say about it?'

'We haven't discussed it.'

'Well, I'd have thought coping with his death – whatever the cause – is a damn sight easier than coping with the idea of him being incarcerated in some mental home for the next thirty years.'

'Perhaps he won't be. Perhaps he'll get . . . fostered.'

'Depends on the shape he's in, surely? How low grade. Did the paediatrician say how bad he was in that respect?'

She shook her head.

'Maybe that's something you should suss out. So everyone knows where you stand if it turns out he does need an operation.'

'But there's still a difference isn't there?' she said, and then hesitated. She was looking at the glowing tip of his cigarette, working it out in her mind. 'Just because we don't want him ourselves, it doesn't mean we've got the right to say he should die, does it?'

'Sounds like your usual soggy liberal get-out clause to me.'

She flushed in anger and he leant forward, so that his face was almost touching hers.

'Look, you've talked about lotteries and fate. Right. OK. Well, fate's handed you a blow, but it's still left you with a choice. It's not like having a car crash or losing your sight or losing a limb, where you've just got to live with it. You knew you didn't have to live with this, so you made a choice. You said no. Now, if fate then says he can't live without an operation, it's giving you another choice. You can either be consistent with your first decision and say no again, or you can say yes and let other people take the consequences of that decision by looking after him for the rest of his life.'

He spoke with an emotion which was unlike him, though as she suspected he must sound in the courtroom: he was confronting her now as if she were a witness.

'Maybe it won't come to that,' she said, aware she was disappointing him, but refusing to admit the implication of his words. He leant back in his chair. He was examining her almost ironically.

'I thought you said you wanted to see the whole experience through?'

'I do.'

'Then why duck the issue?'

'I'm not. I'm still thinking about it. Christ, I only had him two days ago!'

Her voice shook and his expression abruptly altered, moulding into one of concern. It's all rhetoric to him, she thought, just another ethical dilemma to store up for future reference in his legal brain.

He seemed to sense what was in her mind, for he was

leaning forward again, his hands stretched out towards her, palms upwards in a kind of hungry supplication.

'I'm sorry. I'm being very unfeeling.'

'No, not at all.'

'Forgive me?'

'Of course. Don't be silly.'

He said nothing to this, but sat, his body bent towards her, his eyes searching her face.

'Don't underrate yourself, Judith. You've already done the last thing anyone would have expected of you. Don't go soft on it now.'

His tone was brisk and affectionately commanding. She felt humiliated and then angry at the persistence of his intrusion; yet also grateful that he persisted.

'Anyway, for the time being, you're still his mother and Patrick's his father. You're probably right, there'll be other things to think about first. Like registering his birth, all that.'

'I know.'

She was sullen, like a child expecting a reprimand.

'It's just no good, being vague about your motives. That's an indulgence you can't afford right now. It's not over yet, you see.'

She smiled rather wanly. 'I never supposed it was.'

It was nearly two in the morning before he left. She bolted the front door after him and put the chain on. Then she bolted the back door and checked that all the downstairs windows were locked. Only when she was quite satisfied that the house was secure did she go to bed.

Chapter Fourteen

People are very kind, they said to each other during the course of the next few days. The telephone rang only occasionally, but every post brought flowers and letters and cards expressing sympathy. They came from friends and relatives and half-remembered acquaintances. Some referred to tragedies in their own lives, and spoke in well-intentioned clichés about the patterns of grief. These were stilted and full of endearments. Others contrived a more cheerful note, offering carefully selected words of wisdom and support and invitations to stay weekends. The decision was delicately avoided in all but one letter, which was forthright in its criticism. It was from a maiden aunt of Judith's who had maintained a dutiful contact over the years. She condemned the decision in short, blunt sentences. 'One does not return imperfect children,' she wrote, 'like a pair of shoes which do not fit.' A second letter swiftly followed this one, apologising for the tone of the first. The apologies were repeated and heartfelt, yet somehow managed not to rescind a word. Judith put these two letters in a separate drawer from the others, where Patrick would not find them.

Cynthia was one of the first to call round. Judith rested on her bed while Cynthia talked with Patrick in the sitting room. Judith could hear the dull rumble of their voices, and now and again Patrick's slightly raised but still inaudible, and then Cynthia's abrasive yet cajoling reply, clearly placating him. A few minutes later she heard Cynthia's footsteps on the stairs and the bedroom door opened. Her mother's eyes were heavy and thoughtful, the tip of her tongue visible between her lips. The threadbare duffel coat looked incongruous in the feminine, muted ruffles of the bedroom. Cynthia sat beside her on the bed, one hand loosely resting on hers.

'How do you feel?

'All right. A little tired.'

'I'm not surprised. Are you still bleeding a lot?'

Judith smiled inwardly at her mother's customary lack of prevarication.

'A bit. What were you and Patrick talking about?'

'Nothing important.' She sounded vague. She looked around the bedroom, as if noticing it for the first time. She had not been inside it before.

'He says you've been marvellous. A real tower of strength.'

Judith shrugged the remark aside.

'You're certainly taking it very well.'

'I'm taking it, I don't know about well.'

'You're not going under, put it like that.' Cynthia's tone was impatient, as if her thoughts were elsewhere.

'People have worse things happen. They lose entire families, this is nothing compared to that, is it?'

'It's enough to be going on with, I'd have thought.'

'Yes. It's that of course.'

Cynthia rose, her hands back in her pockets. 'You're tired. I'm disturbing you.'

'Not at all.'

'I just wish I could help in some way.'

She invested the words with a thrust of wistfulness, which made Judith uneasy.

'I'm sure there'll be things you can do. When the time comes.'

Cynthia opened her mouth to speak but clamped it closed as Patrick entered. Judith caught a look passing between them, of warning, at least on Patrick's part, and an uncharacteristic forbearance on the part of her mother. She bridled in unease again and wondered why. They stood about the bed a moment, talking. Cynthia looked older, her face more gaunt. Judith remembered how, as a child, men would turn to look at her mother in the street; at her flamboyant dresses and confident, swinging gait. No one would look at her now. After a moment Cynthia said she was due at the hospital, she must go.

'For another check up?'

'Yes, as it happens.'

Judith searched her mother's face for a clue and gave up.

'It was good of you to come.'

'I'll come again tomorrow.'

She leant down and their lips briefly touched. Patrick took her down to the front door, where she could hear them quietly talking once more, before Cynthia left. She lay in bed, listening to the sound of Patrick washing up in the kitchen. She thought of her mother visiting the hospital outpatients, and of the baby, a few floors above in the nursery. There seemed to be an irony there, but she couldn't think about it. She wished the paediatrician would call with the results of the blood test; she knew she could not hold out much longer without one of Patrick's sleeping pills unless he did.

Patrick, washing up in the kitchen, was reflecting upon his conversation with Cynthia. They had discussed the baby, or rather Cynthia had. She had asked if they were quite resolved in their decision and when he said yes she had remarked, 'Well, perhaps it might ease things for you if I took him on.' He had stared at her, and she had then explained to him that at least that way they would know the baby was being properly cared for, which was surely better than thinking of him growing up in some anonymous institution. He had been too taken aback to respond immediately and she had used his silence to pursue her point. She said it would be company for her and give her a purpose again. She said they could visit him, if they felt inclined, safe in the knowledge that they wouldn't be burdened with the long-term care of him. He had sat, shaking his head in disbelief at what she was saying. The whole notion was absurd, of course, and he told her so, adding that Judith would never consent to it. At this Cynthia had become more tenacious; she spoke of their responsibility as parents, that they had no right to deprive him of a decent home if someone was prepared to take him on.

He was apprehensive, more at her tone than her words. He could think of nothing to say. There were gaping holes in the logic of her argument, but he couldn't rally sufficiently to articulate his own arguments against them. Her keen, intelligent eyes watched him continually and this too made him apprehensive. He had always been fond of Cynthia and had considered Judith's antipathy towards her unreasonable; now he began to suspect he had been wrong to dismiss it so lightly. He felt weak and helpless and confused. He told her he couldn't possibly discuss it until Judith was fit again, she was still far from strong. This was unanswerable, and Cynthia reluctantly conceded it. He was relieved. She would forget it in a day or two, as she forgot all her mad schemes. When she had gone he took a Valium and busied himself in the kitchen.

There was something else on Patrick's mind, which was the prospect of returning to work. He didn't know why this should bother him, but it did. It made him uncomfortable to feel this because he had always enjoyed his job, yet he knew it wasn't the job that was making him anxious but the prospect of seeing his colleagues. He had spoken to one or two of them on the telephone, and also to the senior partner of the firm and his wife Elisabeth. They had showered him with sympathy over the baby but Elisabeth had confounded him by saying she had made the baby some clothes and where should she send them? He had been lost for words then also. He told her he thought the baby was still in the hospital, and would be, he imagined, until they had finalised the care situation.

He added, awkward and embarrassed, though he didn't know why, that perhaps it would be better if she didn't send anything, as it might complicate matters. It might be interpreted as parental interest which might, in turn, throw doubt on their decision. Elisabeth listened to him without speaking and he imagined her, luxurious and ample and maternal, frowning in perplexity over his words. She simply said she would do nothing to aggravate what must already be a very painful situation, and hung up. It seemed to him that he heard resentment in her voice.

And he noticed too, that he was getting jumpy. When the phone or the doorbell rang, his nerves would jangle and his hands shake. The Valium helped but he was going through them at an awful lick. He glanced at the calendar on the kitchen wall and was comforted. He could see the months carefully spaced out in their individual boxes, and a pencilled circle around the date of Judith's delivery. It was simply a question of soldiering on until a couple more of those boxes were between them and the pencilled circle, and then everything would be settled: by then his nerves would have steadied, the baby would be safely installed in some . . . his mind faltered . . . foster home or handicapped nursery or wherever they sent such babies. His thoughts turned to the baby in the doctor's surgery and he felt a stab of unfairness which was almost like pain. He wished Judith would cry. He saw her face as the paediatrician told her about the baby, he saw her cheeks go as white as the sheets and he heard her give that hard, piercing little gasp, but she had not cried, and still she had not. If she cried she could release the pain, but she refused to do so. She hung on to it, stubbornly, allowing it to feed on itself and be replenished, making his seem trivial and unimportant by comparison. He saw in her strength now only his own weakness, and he blamed her for it. After a few minutes he felt the welcome sensation of the pain diffusing, as his brain took on its customary numbness. The Valium was starting to work.

⁑ ⁑ ⁑

When Cynthia had finished in the gynaecology clinic, she followed the signs to the maternity block. She walked up the corridor where Judith's ward had been and stood for a second, undecidedly, before approaching a nurse writing at a wedge-shaped desk which jutted out into the passageway.

'Perhaps you can help me. I'm the mother of a patient who was discharged the day before yesterday ... Mrs Fielding.'

The nurse looked up at her. She had sallow skin and dark, beady eyes peering from beneath a heavy fringe. A sign on her lapel said she was a midwife.

'Yes?'

'I'd like to see my grandson. If he's still here. Just for a moment.'

The nurse regarded her suspiciously.

'Did Mrs Fielding ask you to come?'

'No, no. She doesn't know I'm here.' She paused and then added, unneccessarily 'He is my grandson.'

'Wait a moment please.'

The nurse rose from the desk and went through a door marked 'Private'. Cynthia tapped her fingers impatiently. A woman with a squint in an orange dressing gown was limping down the corridor towards her, humming. An orderly was cleaning the floor with a mop in wide practised strokes, expertly swinging her weight from foot to foot. The woman with the squint passed in front of the orderly, watching in fascination as the mop glided over the glistening surface of the floor. Cynthia watched, wondering who it was the nurse was talking to, who it was who had to grant permission for her to see her own grandchild. Just then the nurse came back.

'The paediatrician is on a ward round. He says he'd be happy to talk to you in about half an hour. Room 103.'

'I don't want to see him, I simply want to see my grandchild.'

The nurse looked at her with a kind of flat curiosity, as if weighing her up.

'Mrs Fielding is your daughter?'

'Yes, I said.'

'Have the social workers seen her yet?'

'I couldn't say, I don't think so.' Cynthia masked her impatience with a small, quick smile. 'I'm here entirely on my own volition, no one need know. It won't do any harm, surely? Just for a moment.'

The nurse stared at her. Then she gave a small indifferent shrug.

'He's in the nursery. We expect him to be transferred at any time. You're lucky to catch him.'

She moved around the desk and led the way back up the corridor towards a glass partition. Inside, Cynthia could see a row of cribs containing sleeping babies.

'He's at the end, by the radiator.'

Cynthia followed the nurse's pointing finger. She faintly recognised the tip of the baby's head, peeping out of a blue shawl.

'Can I go in?'

'It's mothers only. I'm sorry.'

'Is there somewhere you can bring him then? So I can see him properly? Hold him perhaps?'

'I'll see. Wait please.'

She padded off. Cynthia stood, eyeing her grandchild through the window of the nursery. She glanced at the other babies. From where she was, she could discern no difference between them. Unaccountably, this upset her, and she struggled to keep a grip on her emotions. She moved further up the window, so that she was nearer to the baby, looking directly down at him, but her breath on the window masked her view of him. She felt like a child with its face pressed against the window of a sweet shop. She turned away to see the nurse returning, bearing a paper robe ahead of her, like a shield.

'It's quite in order, but only for a minute. You'll have to wear this. We like to keep the nursery sterile.'

Cynthia smiled at the choice of words but silently shed her duffel coat and slid into the paper gown. It had the look of a shroud about it. The nurse led her into the nursery. The baby was asleep. He looked larger than she remembered. She crouched down by the basinette so that her face was only an inch or so from his. He was snorting gently as he breathed, his mouth slightly open.

'Is he feeding well?'

'Slow and steady, you know. Do you want me to get him out?'

'No . . . since he's asleep. Best not disturb him.'

He had a mat of fine, downy fair hair. The bridge of his nose was quite flat, the tip of it rising, like a button mushroom, out of the swelling of his cheeks. She examined him carefully, scrupulously, assessing her own reactions as she did. This was important.

'I thought his tongue would be larger. I thought that was one of the characteristics.'

'That comes later apparently.'

'I see, yes.'

She crouched a second longer, observing him without touching him. She wished his eyes would open but still felt disinclined to wake him. The nurse stood behind her, watching, as if she too was assessing her reactions. Cynthia straightened up.

'Thank you.'

'Not at all.'

They went back into the corridor where Cynthia exchanged the gown for her duffel coat.

'She still feels the same, does she? Mrs Fielding?'

'Yes, it would seem so.'

'It's a shame. She never really gave herself a chance.'

'I assume she didn't want to.'

Cynthia felt a sharp nudge of loyalty to Judith, imagining her facing those beady, clinical eyes. She thanked the nurse again and left, nearly colliding with the woman in the orange dressing gown. The woman looked momentarily startled, one eye lurching upwards, the other gazing blankly into Cynthia's, who apologised before quickly moving off to the lift. Eyes, she thought, eyes everywhere. She didn't feel like going home yet, she had too much to think about. And the youth at the café would only distract her, so that was out. She would go to the park for a walk and imagine herself there with the baby in the pushchair, for she might be asked about this and should be prepared. She would imagine heads turning to look not at her but at the baby, and yet more eyes, glazing slightly, as realisation dawned and they looked away in embarrassed sympathy. She swung out of the hospital and took a bus to the nearest park. There were people lying there in couples and in groups and no one took any notice of her. She decided, after all, to go to the café.

*　　*　　*

On the third day after she had been discharged from hospital Judith was telephoned by a social worker. Her voice was young and springing with confidence. She said she was a medical social worker from the hospital, ringing in connection with the baby. She arranged to call that afternoon.

She arrived promptly and Patrick ushered her into the sitting room. She was small and dark, wearing a plaid coat with a hood, and black stockings which gave her a deceptively casual, artistic look. She sat with her legs wrapped around each other, a small notebook on her lap, a patent leather yellow handbag, shaped like a satchel, on the floor beside her. The sight of it annoyed Judith. She imagined the girl in a pub, surrounded by young and laughing faces, the satchel slung over one shoulder, having a well-deserved drink after a day of finding homes for rejected mongols. It was a hard, bitter little thought, and Judith rebuked herself for thinking it, yet it nagged at her while they talked. It was not the girl she resented, or even her job as such, but the fact that they were now a problem to be filed and categorised and forgotten at the end of the day.

She asked initially about the baby, his hour and date of delivery, whether Judith had suspected anything of his condition herself, how she had felt when she had been told about him. Judith replied in considered, precise sentences, Patrick occasionally filling in details. The girl took notes as they talked, and went on to ask about themselves, their ages, whether or not they owned the house, and what was Patrick's profession. When Judith admitted she had none, the pencil paused over the notebook, the same thought in all their minds.

'I intend to get a job,' Judith said quickly, aware that her tone was defensive, and resentful that it should be.

'Doing what?'

'Infant teaching, I suppose, it's what I'm trained to do.'

'You're good with children, are you?'

The question sounded like another trap and Judith squared herself before replying.

'Reasonably.'

'Do you intend to have other children?'

'If we can. If the genetic thing is all right.'

'You're still waiting to hear that?'

'Yes.'

'It must be very difficult.'

'Yes.'

The girl uncrossed her legs and fiddled with the pencil.

'You have a lovely home,' she stated.

Judith flashed her a look of pure hatred.

'Yes,' she said again, this time framing it like a challenge. The girl lowered her eyes.

'There are other options,' she said, 'other than the one you've taken. You could take him home for a few days, a few weeks even, just to see how things go.'

'No.'

'Some kind of partial care perhaps then. So the responsibility is shared.'

'No.'

'You'd get plenty of outside support, Mrs Fielding. There are specialist agencies which could help you.'

'No.'

'You really should consider all the alternatives, really you should.'

'And where would they be, your specialist agencies, when we want someone to babysit for us when he's fourteen so we can go out by ourselves? Where will they be when we want to go shopping, go anywhere without everyone staring at us? Where will they be in the middle of the night when he has tantrums and we can't cope? I'll tell you where they'll be, at the end of a telephone mouthing platitudes, telling us to make an appointment or fill in a form!' Judith was gripping the arms of her chair. She was aware of Patrick jerking his foot up and down, staring at it.

'It's not always as bad as that.'

'Not if you're on the outside looking in, no.'

'I can't change the world, Mrs Fielding. The way things are, the way people are. Coming to terms with mental handicap is a very complex thing, for anyone.'

'I appreciate that.'

'The kind of support you want, it may be possible. I

honestly don't know. There's an association for parents of handicapped children like yours. I could make enquiries. If something like it were possible. If you could be satisfied it was, would you reconsider your decision?'

'No.'

'You wouldn't even think about it?'

'No.'

'Then that can't be the sole reason.'

'Obviously not.'

'Do you want to talk about what you think the real reason could be?'

'No.'

'I want to help you, Mrs Fielding.'

'Help me change my mind or help arrange his care?'

'However I can.'

'You can help by working out where he's going, then. Whatever the next step is.'

'I want to be sure first that you're certain about the step you've already taken.'

'I am certain.'

'Both of you?'

Patrick glanced up at this point, his foot momentarily halting.

'Oh, yes, absolutely.'

'Have either of you had anything to do with mentally handicapped children before?'

'We've come across them, as one does.' This was from Judith.

'Then you'll know they can be very rewarding. That they can have a lot to offer. That the picture isn't wholly bad.'

'From your point of view I'm sure it isn't.'

'Mrs Fielding . . . '

The girl's face was peaked in earnestness.

'People talk about their potential,' Judith interjected in

a carefully moderated tone. 'They don't talk about their potential to wreck families and break up marriages, do they?'

'Perhaps because that's not always the case. Particularly if a marriage or a family is a strong one.'

Judith smiled at her grimly.

'You've got an answer for everything, haven't you?'

'I'm trying to help you find some answers. You're being so pessimistic about the outlook. Some of them can lead virtually normal lives. They can go to school. Do most of the things normal children do.'

Judith said nothing for a moment; then she said:

'And some of them don't learn to walk until they're seven or eight and never learn to speak at all.'

'But who's to say your son will be like that?'

'Can anyone tell me categorically, without a doubt, that he won't be?'

'I imagine it's impossible to say at this stage. It's the degree of handicap, is it, which worries you?'

Judith made no reply, she was afraid now that her answers might ensnare her more than the questions. A short silence fell. The social worker turned a page of the notebook.

'I know you find it hard to believe now, Mrs Fielding, but you could come to love him in time.'

Judith felt her mouth go dry.

'You're not married are you?' she asked.

'No ... '

'I take it then you've got no children?'

The girl was surprised by the question and showed it.

'No ... but I don't see that ... '

'Have you handled a case like this before?'

'No.' This was in defeat.

'It's rather like the blind leading the blind then, isn't it?'

The girl's face was crimson. Judith felt tears of anger and then self reproach sting the back of her eyes.

'I'm sorry,' she said, and then again. 'I'm sorry.'

'Please, it doesn't matter.'

Patrick's foot was still jerking, his eyes vacant. The girl was rotating the pencil between her thumb and fore-finger. Through the open door to the kitchen Judith could hear the steady, rhythmic tick of the clock on the cooker.

'Do you prepare the care order papers, or what?'

'My department will do it, in conjunction with the local authority. I think that's the procedure. There might be other people to see first, I'm afraid.'

'I see. Right.'

The girl was making notes again, thin spidery scrawls between the lines on her pad. She said she would research the various channels of care and come back to them. She stood up to go, her cheeks still flaming. Patrick escorted her to the door, where they briefly said goodbye. When Patrick returned he stood looking at her a moment, his face hard.

'You were very unpleasant, you should have heard yourself.'

'I did.'

'Why must you make things so deliberately diffi-cult?'

'I thought you wanted it settled?'

'Not like that.'

'I haven't done this sort of thing before, perhaps next time I'll be better.'

His eyes were angry now, his face twisted in annoy-ance.

'You're just being totally irrational about the whole thing.'

'I've never felt more rational in my life.'

'You're behaving like a cold-blooded cow, and you know it.'

'What we're doing isn't particularly nice, Patrick. There's no point in pretending it is, and making polite small talk.'

'And there's also no point in antagonising these people. We want to keep them on our side.'

'You admit there are sides then?'

'Judith.' He said it wearily, as if exhausted. 'You're just not being fair.'

'Who in God's name expects anything to be fair?'

With this she left the room, to lie on the bed upstairs. But a moment later she went back downstairs again. She wanted to tell him she was hard and ruthless because she was frightened. She wanted him to hold her and hear him say that he understood. She felt no pride about this, because the feeling of it was so intense it overcame her pride. But she pushed open the sitting room door to find him on the telephone to his mother. 'Oh, Judith handled it all,' he was saying. 'I wasn't allowed a word in. Mind you, in her present mood it's probably a good thing. Everything I say or do at the moment is . . . '

She closed the door and went back upstairs. Every day he spoke to his mother on the telephone, devouring her simple, amiable advice, and then repeating it to her so that she almost thought his mother was there in the house with them. She lay on the bed. His jar of Valium was on the bedside table. She regarded it a minute, and then turned so that her back was towards it. She would telephone Chris when Patrick was off the phone and ask him round. He would bring wine and tell them jokes and make them laugh as he always could.

Chapter Fifteen

The following Monday Patrick returned to work. They were kept busy the preceding weekend by household chores and on the Saturday evening Chris called round with the intention of taking them out to dinner. Patrick, however, pleaded tiredness and it was agreed they would stay in instead. They ate a Chinese takeaway and played backgammon, and got mildy drunk and Chris stayed the night in the spare bedroom. They spoke briefly about the baby at the beginning of the evening, when Chris enquired about the social worker's visit. They glanced at each other and Patrick said Judith had handled her superbly and Chris grinned at her in open appreciation and said he never had any doubt but that she would. She observed that his manner was altered with her, he seemed slightly awed by her, mingled with an affecting, respectful concern.

On Sunday morning Chris drove them to his Oxfordshire cottage. Judith sat in the back and they sang old Beatles numbers and argued about the harmonics, and the thought sprang into her mind that she was happy, and they wouldn't be doing this if they'd had a baby with them. They had a pub lunch and spent the afternoon in front of the fire reading the Sunday newspapers. They were relaxed and pleasantly at ease and in the few moments when Patrick and Judith were alone they acknowledged this, in mute relief.

In the evening Chris and Judith cooked a meal, while Patrick sat listening to the Elgar cello concerto in the living room. It was an old converted gamekeeper's cottage, beamed and solidly built, with small deep-set windows which afforded a magnificent view of uninterrupted fields and hedgerows. Judith poured some wine and carried a glass through to Patrick. He was sitting by the window, sobbing. Quickly she closed the door which separated them from the kitchen and knelt next to him. The sight of his tears moved her to an unfamiliar tenderness. He put his head on her shoulder and cried, hiccoughing and gasping in an attempt to control himself. She did not speak but simply held him, rocking him in her arms. Eventually his sobs died away; she felt him go quite limp under her touch.

'What was it?' she asked.

'Oh, the music. It's so beautiful and intelligent. And he'll never appreciate it, will he? Not properly.'

'No.'

He gulped and moved away from her, pressing his knuckles into his eyes.

'Maybe he will,' she conceded, seeing the tears threaten again. 'Who can say? They're supposed to like music, aren't they?'

'I'm not talking about that kind of appreciation, am I?'

'No, I suppose not.'

'And even if he did like it, no one's going to do much about it are they? In an institution.'

A switch turned inside her and she pulled herself up so that she was standing over him.

'And knowing that the kind of appreciation you want isn't there, you wouldn't do anything about it if he was at home, would you? So what's the difference?'

Before he could speak she felt inside his jacket pocket for the Valium. She waited until he'd taken one before she moved to the record player and switched off the music, and returned to the kitchen to help Chris with the preparations for supper.

Late that night Chris drove them home. Judith lay awake for some time, her mind keen and self-absorbed. When she woke the next morning Patrick had already left for work.

Chapter Fifteen

On the Monday afternoon a second social worker called round. He was older than the first, and taller, his lined face showing signs of strain. He sat in the same seat as the first social worker, drinking tea. He did not use a notebook. He was cautious and tentative in his questions and she suspected he had been forewarned. She attempted to adopt a politely deferential manner, which she hoped would appear less aggressive, more full of quiet resolve. She was relieved by Patrick's absence for it gave her a free hand to manoeuvre around his questions and, where necessary, to fabricate her answers. One fabrication concerned Anthony. She had been asked if she had ever known any other mongols, (except he used the term 'Down's syndrome', which was an expression which continued to rankle with her; she regarded it as an evasion). In reply to his question she had told him about working in the café with Anthony.

'There are different grades, you know. Anthony might have been a very low grade type.'

'You make them sound like that advertisement for flour.'

'I'm sorry?'

'Graded grains make finer flour.'

She did not know what possessed her to say this, and instantly regretted it. He stared at her, appalled and then perplexed at the inappropriateness of it.

'I was going to suggest that maybe you should see other Down's children. I'm sure we could arrange something. So you can see all the possibilities and have a more informed view.'

'No, thank you.'

'They are all individuals, Mrs Fielding. Your son could be quite different from Anthony.'

'Worse or better?'

'Different. He'll inherit some characteristics from you and your husband, won't he?'

119

'Are you telling me or asking me?'

'It's a fact, I'd have thought.'

'He's still a mongol.'

She said it unwillingly and he seemed to sense this.

'He's also still a child. Your child.'

'I know. And I know that I should be responsible for him. Intellectually I know this. But I'm afraid I also feel people are a little too quick to capitalise on it.'

He frowned at this, his manner altering.

'Is that what you think I'm doing?'

'I think you believe a lot of what you're saying. About him being better off in a family and all that. But I think you're also saying it so that you and the hospital and the local authority can offload the responsibility of him. Which is of course what I'm doing, so I can hardly criticise.'

He shifted his weight in the chair. He was clearly surprised at her words, as indeed she was, though she surprised herself less and less these days.

'I believe it's part of my job to ensure you've chosen the right course of action. For yourself and the baby.'

'I've made that choice, haven't I? And I have a right to make it, although nobody's bothered to point that out.'

She smiled at him quickly to take the sting out of the words, and then added, as if to close the subject: 'Anyway, I worked in a handicapped home as a student. Another holiday job. So you see I saw all grades of them. High and low, all shapes and sizes in fact.'

This was a lie but she felt quite safe in it. Again she got an apprehensive look from him, as if he was afraid she was mocking him, and she arranged her face good-naturedly to show that she wasn't. He swallowed the remainder of his tea and left. She stood at the window watching as he strode to his car. He sat inside it for some time, his head bent. Taking notes, she thought, mother highly-strung and hostile, but clearly determined. She imagined a line of columns on a form, and her name above it, and a stamp coming down on it and the form being pushed into a file marked 'Pending'. She moved into the kitchen and looked for another cupboard to clean.

*   *   *

The office was quiet on his first day back and Patrick's colleagues diffident and discreet in their contact with him. The journey to work, however, had been a nightmare. He had got claustrophobic on the tube and had to get out and take a bus, which made him late. He arrived at the office trembling and limp with strain. He took another Valium, which calmed him, but made it difficult to concentrate. Judith rang him during the morning to say another social worker, a man this time, was coming to see her. Once again he felt his heart race and his hands shake. He had an awful vision of the social worker bringing the baby with him. He imagined the social worker ringing the front door bell, the baby in his arms, and Judith reaching out, despite herself, to accept it. And he would return home to find it installed in the nursery and Judith's former resolve now reversed, like the swing of a pendulum, into a new determination to keep him. He knew this to be unlikely, but felt at the same time that it was not impossible: there was a lot about Judith's behaviour nowadays that he would have once thought impossible. He sat morosely at his desk trying to focus his attention on his work, and failing.

At lunchtime he went to the pub across the road with his colleagues, but made an excuse to return to the office early where he telephoned Judith to find out what had transpired. She was cleaning out a cupboard, she said, the social worker had just left. She repeated some of the interview to him and he felt vaguely encouraged. He then made another telephone call, to a private doctor, and made an appointment to see him the following day. He needed more Valium and he was anxious that his medical record should not state this fact; he felt, obscurely, it might count against him at some future date. As he did this he recognised once again that he was being petty in his priorities, and this increased his feeling of self-disgust. Just then his colleagues returned from the pub and straddled the desks around him, discussing the forthcoming office football match and who they should select as captain and he was able, with a little perseverance, to lose himself in the conversation.

Later that afternoon Judith tackled the nursery with Wanda. Together they dismantled the cot and got out the stepladder and hauled the cot and mattress and the baby clothes, now wrapped in a polythene laundry bag, into the loft. There was also a baby bouncer and the playpen to dispose of, and Wanda asked if she could lend them to a friend who was expecting a baby, and strapped them on to her roof-rack and drove off to deliver them. After she had gone, Judith made tea and sat in the kitchen drinking it, thinking about her mother. She was still perplexed by her unexplained visits to the hospital. The thought came into her mind that her mother had cancer and the possibility pierced her suddenly like a splinter. She knew it to be a morbid idea but she could not entirely dismiss it.

She hovered hesitantly over the telephone, wondering whether to ring Cynthia and confront her with her suspicions, but decided against it. Cynthia would only laugh at her fears and she would then bridle in resentment, as she always did. She realised that her hands were sweating and that she must be frightened. But of what? Losing her mother or confronting her?

She caught sight of herself in the mirror, her face pinched with anxiety, and collected herself. She was being quite ridiculous. She imagined Cynthia saying that to her, and immediately felt better. She must stop her mind from dwelling on such foolish, macabre ideas. Thinking this, she put on her coat and went for a walk. It was the first time she had been out alone since she had left the hospital. The sight of babies and prams in the street jolted her, as it had done Patrick, but more because she hadn't anticipated them rather than because they served as a reminder. She eyed them warily as she walked past them, and was surprised that she felt so little. She had never been broody over other people's babies and she was glad to see that she hadn't changed. She even felt a little proud of herself, as she had when she had stripped the nursery; proud that she hadn't allowed such obviously potent emotional events to have any more than a passing impact on her. She regarded them like dramatic moments in a play, in which she was an observer rather than a participant. It was simply a trick of the mind, she decided, like operating a lever in one's head, and she was puzzled when her thoughts drifted, unasked, once more to Cynthia, to find that in this one respect the lever was less efficient.

Wanda called round that evening. She was flushed and angry, her mood alternating between aggression and thinly-veiled tears.

'We've been burgled,' she exclaimed as soon as she entered. 'It must have been this afternoon while I was round here helping you, Judith.'

There was something faintly accusatory about the way she said this, and she seemed to sense it, for she sped on, anxious not to prolong the moment.

'He got in through the back door, just smashed the window and undid the lock. It's a wonder we didn't hear him.'

Patrick pressed a drink into her hand and she took it, brandishing the glass as she spoke.

'He took a transistor radio and some cassettes. Plus all

my jewellery of course, and every penny in the house. The bastard.'

'Have you phoned the police?'

'Oh yes, they sent someone round. Some pimply, bloody youth who stood about drinking tea and asking a lot of irrelevant questions. Straight out of training school, I shouldn't wonder. It's the idea of him in the house. Going through our things, touching them.'

She shuddered and gulped her drink. Judith and Patrick sat next to each other on the sofa, saying nothing.

'I got the glazier in to see to the window before the kids came home from school. With a bit of luck they won't notice anything's gone, except the radio. I'll say I dropped it or something.'

Judith thought of Wanda's children, loud and vulgar, chalking graffiti on the garage wall and lobbing apple cores over the fence, and Wanda's vain efforts to protect them from within, with glaziers and private tuition.

'The policeman said all this area is getting done. Particularly houses like ours. Something to do with not being overlooked at the back.'

'Oh God, that's all we need.'

This was from Patrick, and Wanda glanced at him as if recollecting that they, too, had a grievance.

'It's unlikely he'll come back to do you, isn't it? Not right next door. Too risky.'

She paced the floor, her bulky, powerful frame towering over them.

'What gets me is why, though? Why pick our house? There are plenty of others, why did it have to be us?'

No one answered the question. A few seconds later she apologised for making so much of it and had another drink, which seemed to calm her; then she left.

As they locked up that night Patrick commented that perhaps they should look again at their own security. The next day he sent off for catalogues on burglar alarm systems and then decided it was a job he could do perfectly well himself. He bought new locks for the windows and doors and several ultrasonic devices which would detect the presence of an intruder, and set about placing them in strategic points about the house. It proved to be a more complex job than he envisaged, requiring extensive rewiring and mounting of bells, both inside and out, as well as siting and fixing the ultrasonic detectors, and the fitting of new locks. However, he tackled the project with something like his old enthusiasm, and became quite absorbed in it, even managing to whip Judith into a dutiful appreciation of his efforts. It took over a week to complete, working in the evenings and the weekend, and at the end of that time he persuaded Judith to pretend to be a burglar so as to test the system out. Feeling somewhat ridiculous, but curious to see what would happen, she opened a kitchen window and climbed through. As her foot touched the kitchen floor she was greeted by a deafening crescendo of ringing bells, and Patrick's jubilant face, shouting incoherently at her that the system worked. Clearly it did. The house was now invulnerable.

Chapter Sixteen

Cynthia was also trying to put her house in order, or at any rate her books. She sat at the circular table in her unused dining room, surrounded by old bank statements and cheque stubs, totting up figures and then adding them again in the hope that her first calculation had been wrong.

She was endeavouring to get her books in order so that she could prove, if necessary, that she was financially solvent. She made a note to remind herself to check whether she would be eligible for the baby's child allowance, for she was anxious to appear practical when the time came to make her application. She had not yet discovered which body or department would handle such an application and was waiting for a call from her solicitor friend to find that out. In this one thing she was determined to be methodical and thorough.

When she had finally made the figures come out the way she wanted, she poured herself a drink and strolled around the house. She tried to visualise it with someone else's eyes. Many of the rooms had not been used for several years and smelt dank and musty. Her furniture, now she came to look at it, was ill-assorted and delapidated. Hinges were broken off bureaux, the flaps propped up by books; handles were missing from chests of drawers, the mirrors in the wardrobes were cracked and mottled.

She ambled through the house, opening doors and peering into cupboards until eventually she came to the room which had once been occupied by Judith. There were five bedrooms in all and this one was the smallest; it was at the back, overlooking the garden.

Except for a single bed, lacking in a mattress, it was completely empty. There was a fitted wardrobe in one corner, and that too was empty. She stood, shaken by the sudden clarity of the memories of Judith which now assaulted her. She had entered the room, speculating on whether or not it would be accepted as suitable for the child, but the idea now seemed grotesque and offensive. She quickly went out and back downstairs. The unwilling realisation came upon her that what she was proposing to do was abhorrent and quite awful.

She sat in the kitchen for a while, her head in her hands,

trying to discipline her thoughts. She had to have the baby, she knew this with complete conviction. But the wanting of him was all mixed up with the sense of unease, of wishing to make amends. But would Judith ever understand this? Would she ever forgive her? Had she the right to expect forgiveness? Cynthia wrestled with the various trains of thought in her mind, examining each next step as it occurred to her. Eventually she got up and returned to the dining room, as if trying to put a distance between herself and the problem. Just then the telephone rang. It was her solicitor friend, saying he would help her in any way he could. He took some details and said he would research into the case and call her again. She replaced the telephone with a mixture of elation and self-loathing, persuading herself that it was now too late to go back.

*   *   *

There was one further session with the social workers, who came together. The interview was strained but cordial and Patrick took the afternoon off so that he could be present. The social workers broached the decision once again, navigating their way carefully around it, each one taking their cue from the other. There was something pre-rehearsed about it, which neither Patrick nor Judith resented as the pattern of the questions was by now so familiar that they had already rehearsed their replies.

Patrick took the car to work every day, as the prospect of the tube had become intolerable and the bus too unreliable. However, even in the car he felt vulnerable and tense. This was heightened by a tingling of pins and needles in his left hand, and a tightening of the muscles across his chest which made it painful for him to breathe. Whenever this feeling took possession of him, he would pull the car off the road and park and sit listening to the radio until the sensation passed. His dread of the feeling seemed actually to initiate it; he felt himself caught in a chain of reactions of his own making, which seemed to further exasperate things, for he knew he had no control over it.

He had mentioned something of this to Judith, who had been brisk and practical in her response, saying it was a typical symptom of stress. She had heard all about it on a radio phone-in (she listened to phone-ins a lot these days) and she told him he should take more exercise and let the tensions work themselves out that way. It was sound, sensible advice but he ignored it.

Ostensibly, the old threads of their life had been picked up, although Patrick was disinclined to go out; even the sight of the car accentuated his anxiety. They invited friends round and gave dinner parties and talked openly about the baby to anyone who asked. They found they enjoyed talking about him, and even guided conversations back to the subject whenever they strayed too far from it. They rarely discussed the baby when they were alone, and used their friends, consciously or not, as a means by which they could do so. They knew it to be a not uncommon method of dealing with grief and they felt this both allowed and excused it. Talking about the baby in the presence of others also had the effect of neutralising their emotion; they felt able to voice their feelings without any sense of self-conciousness or self-indulgence. Their friends, too, seemed glad, even somewhat eager, to talk about it, believing themselves to have exclusive access to a dilemma they knew they would not be likely to face. But at the end of these evenings, while washing up and preparing for bed, their friends' assurances that they had done the right thing still ringing in their ears, both Judith and Patrick would feel curiously jaded, as if they had exhausted the topic but still left things unsaid.

Exactly two weeks after Judith's discharge from

hospital, the paediatrician rang to say that the blood tests on the baby had come through; they were defined as the sporadic type. They would almost certainly be able to have a normal child, subject to genetic counselling and Judith having a test during any subsequent pregnancy. They felt quite euphoric after the phone call, and hugged each other, before Patrick broke away and hurried to telephone his parents. Later that evening Judith telephoned Cynthia who was uninhibited in her delight at the news, adding that as soon as Judith's menstrual cycle had re-established itself, she should get pregnant. When Judith demurred, saying that they could do nothing until the situation with the present baby was resolved, Cynthia became quite insistent, adding that the only way they would ever get it resolved was by having another child. At that moment Judith was feeling too pleasant and good-natured to refute the simple logic of this argument and listened in silence to Cynthia until eventually the conversation drifted to its natural conclusion.

They spoke now quite regularly on the telephone. The calls were usually instigated by Cynthia and were generally short and to the point. She would enquire as to Judith's health and state of mind and then ask what news there was on the 'baby front', as she called it; and after saying she would call again the next day, she would hang up. Her calls came at odd times of the day, and sometimes late at night, and they touched Judith. It was a minimal maternal concession but it was enough.

The day after the paediatrician's call, Judith decided to register the birth. Due to Patrick's reluctance to go out, she rarely took any excursions out of the house, except to the local shops, and she prepared herself for this one with some trepidation. She telephoned the town hall first to enquire where to go, set the burglar alarm and reported, as she had been instructed on the telephone, to some chambers in the basement of the civic centre.

A squat, besuited little man beamed at her from behind a leather-embossed desk and ushered her to a chair before bending over the desk to tick her name in a ledger. The room was windowless and painted pale green. The walls were bare except for a seascape on the wall directly behind him. He told her that for only a few pounds she could have a larger, more detailed, birth certificate which would include additional information about the parents and their occupations. When Judith declined this, rather more vigorously than she intended, he opened up a blotter on the desk and showed her an example of the larger birth certificate, pointing out its advantages over the smaller one, which was terse and minimal in comparison, recording only the baby's name and date of birth. He reminded Judith of a doorstep salesman, though she knew he was probably only being kind, but his concerned obsequiousness made her wince, and he seemed to observe this, for he stopped, mid-drift, and pulled out a small, square pink form and started to write on it.

He recorded the date and location of the birth, and, pen poised expectantly over the form, asked her for the baby's full name. She opened her mouth to say 'Jack' and then closed it. She did not know why she did this except that Jack was the name for the child they envisaged they would have, not the one they eventually got. She did not have time to explain it any more fully than this. She searched her mind for alternatives, and the little man waited, pen in hand, restraining his impatience with the fact that she had clearly not applied her mind to this matter before. She was trying to think of a name which had no personal associations for either Patrick or herself, and which would also be appropriate for life in an institution. Yet every name she hit upon seemed like a bad joke when connected with a mongol. Henry . . . Arthur . . . George . . . Oliver . . . The names raced through her brain. Her eyes at this point settled distractedly on the painting of the seascape in front of her. It was crude and amateurish, depicting a swirling sea with a dinghy perched in the middle of it. Underneath was a label on which was typed the painter's name. She could not decipher the surname, but on seeing the Christian name she knew immediately that the problem was solved.

'John,' she said.

He penned the name in with a small flourish, as if sharing her sense of triumph.

'And his second name?'

She was tempted to say none but thought better of it. The absurd notion came into her head that most children have middle names, and she couldn't deprive her child of this one, modest, semblance of normality. Once again an armoury of names marched through her mind. Once again help was at hand. On the desk between them was a small, elevated panel of wood on which was engraved, in gold letters, the name of the official.

'David,' she replied.

If he observed the source of her inspiration, the man showed no indication of it, but quickly inscribed 'David' under the first name. He then signed the certificate and blotted it and handed it to her. She swept it into her handbag and snapped the clasp closed. The man was now scribbling in the ledger in his neat, curved writing. Uncertain whether the process was complete, she waited until eventually he closed the ledger and smiled at her. She thought she saw unease in his expression and tried to imagine how he was interpreting her indifferent and taciturn manner, and then wondered why she should care.

'He's a mongol,' she said, and the man's face quivered with compassion.

'Oh dear. That's very sad.'

'Yes.'

Feeling that the interview was now concluded, she rose and swiftly left the room.

Chapter Seventeen

The burglar alarm system was starting to get on Judith's nerves. Patrick had located the master switch halfway down the cellar stairs and had set the clock on it so that anyone leaving the house had less than thirty seconds to evacuate. There were certain procedures to accomplish first. Every door in the house had to be closed, all the window catches checked, the key to the burglar system located. Only then could the switch be turned. Any delay or hiccough in the proceedings – a door left inadvertently open, the phone ringing after the alarm had been switched on – set the bells off, two on the outside, front and rear, and two inside. Judith decided after several nerve-racking misadventures with the system that she was more frightened of the bells than she ever would be of a burglar. She would sit eyeing the sonic detectors, which winked down at her from the ceiling, contemplating whether or not it was worth the effort to go out at all. More often than not she decided it wasn't. She was, she began to perceive, a prisoner, not simply in her own home, but of Patrick's insecurities.

It was now nearly three weeks since the baby's birth and another fact was beginning to grate on Judith's nerves. They had not yet been visited by Patrick's parents. Although Patrick had spoken to his mother almost nightly on the telephone, and she had heard him repeatedly suggest that they come to London to see them, there had been no indication that they were going to take the invitation up. She began to see the house in Essex in a new light. Whereas previously it had provided a becalmed oasis, a welcome retreat from the pressures of London, she now saw in that calmness only a self-absorbed blandness: the predictable domestic demands Patrick's parents imposed on themselves were an eleborate artefact which imprisoned them as much as the burglar alarm system now imprisoned her. She remembered how Patrick's father only read the sports pages of the newspaper and her own reaction on catching sight of a headline about a murder or another IRA bombing campaign – how remote and fictional these events seemed when viewed from the muffled comfort of Patrick's home.

She had tackled Patrick about his parents and he had clearly shared her unease at their reticence about seeing them, but promptly made allowances, as she knew he would, suggesting that perhaps they were still finding it difficult to cope with their own distress, let alone witnessing theirs. She brushed this excuse aside impatiently, and he refused to discuss the matter further. After this, his telephone calls to his mother became more circumspect. He took to calling her from the office, or from the bedroom when Judith was cooking in the kitchen. These actions did not provoke argument but were tacitly accepted between them: there were many such silent aggravations at that time.

Finally they received a telephone call from the medical social worker's department at the hospital. The care papers for the local authority had been drawn up, and were ready for their signature.

They signed them early one morning. Patrick drove them both to the hospital on his way to work. They found their way to the medical social worker's department, and were instructed to wait in the corridor outside an office.

This section of the hospital, unlike the maternity block, was not modern. It was Victorian, high ceilinged with Gothic overtones, and awesomely institutional. The long echoing corridor was dark, the only source of light coming from several small frosted glass windows scattered intermittently along one wall.

They sat on a chair and waited, Patrick reading the morning paper. Two figures tramped towards them down the corridor. One was a middle-aged woman, immaculately dressed, with made-up eyes and shoes which matched her handbag. With her was an adolescent girl. She was vast and cumbersome, with sores on her hands; her hair straggled about her face and stood out from the back of her head in an angry shock of tangles.

They sat on the vacant chairs beside Judith and Patrick and the girl promptly bowed over, hugging her arms, and started gently rocking to and fro, grunting as she did. The grunts were quiet, as if she were conversing with herself. She was not a mongol, though Judith had to check twice to be sure. The mother of the girl – one sensed she was the mother somehow – sat next to her, her handbag perched on her lap, her fingers, manicured and painted, resting lightly upon it. She maintained a diligent but detached watch on the girl, her chin raised, her attention apparently elsewhere.

Patrick, absorbed in his paper, made no sign that he had registered the presence of either the girl or her mother. Judith smiled inwardly with a kind of rueful triumph. It seemed ironic that the social workers, after all their tactful endeavours to get her to rethink her decision should make this *faux pas* now, at the eleventh hour, when it was still possible for her to change her mind. The presence of the rocking and grunting girl made her feel no guilt but rather served as a confirmation of something she felt she already knew; all she was aware of at that moment was a pervading, almost exhilarating sense of relief.

They briefly read the papers, and signed them in turn. It was the woman social worker who dealt with the matter. Although they had intended to, they did not ask where the baby was, or where he was destined to go, and she did not tell them. When they had completed the formality with the forms, she seemed anxious to talk, but hesitated, sensing their disinclination. She simply said another social worker from the local authority would be in touch with them and shook their hands and wished them luck. The corridor outside the office was now quite empty. The girl and her mother had gone.

The trip into the hospital to sign the order papers told them something they hadn't appreciated before. In the intervals between the vigorous and often quite passionate assertions from their friends that their decision was the correct one, the thought still lingered that what they were doing was intrinsically shameful. By-lines in newspapers and chance remarks about parents cheerfully battling with, and overcoming, the problems of raising handicapped children seemed to confirm this. Yet when the social worker had handed them the papers to sign she had done it resignedly. And the questions on the forms themselves seemed to contain this same note of resignation. It was in the end a bureaucratic procedure. They found something comforting in this, which outweighed the unspoken, unintentional reproaches they seemed to encounter almost daily. As if they were on a road others had negotiated before them, it was simply a question of sticking to it and not allowing their attention to be distracted by those people who had decided to travel in the opposite direction.

Another week passed. Cynthia called round twice in the afternoons while Patrick was at work, on her way to the hospital outpatients. They had tea and talked of family matters and Cynthia's desire to get her house redecorated. When Cynthia left, they embraced warmly and without their usual restraint. The subject of Cynthia's visits to the hospital was not touched upon. Although Judith was still apprehensive as to their cause, she was even more apprehensive of upsetting this new and delicate plateau in their relationship.

Judith discovered that the local grocery store would deliver food and every other day telephoned in her order. Friends still telephoned, though less often now, and most mornings Wanda dropped in for coffee and a chat. Work at the office had picked up and Patrick was generally not home until mid-evening, when he would quickly eat and fall asleep in front of the television. Judith's bleeding was less constant, more erratic; the pills had most satisfactorily dried up her milk and her breasts had gone back to something of their old shape. She was losing weight too, although this didn't please her as it would have once done, it seemed inappropriate somehow to take pleasure in so negligible an achievement. Patrick's stress symptoms persisted, but Valium and a little forethought contained them well enough, and except for the fact that he was still obviously reluctant to go out, it did not inconvenience them unduly.

They had each seen a mongol since the event, One afternoon Judith, crouching in front of the television and turning the knob to change channels, came face to face with a photograph of one. It was the frozen image of a little girl, her hair in bunches, grinning mischievously into the camera and directly into Judith's eyes. A voice-over accompanied the picture, describing the little girl, (her name was Julia), and how she had been adopted and was now the centre of a happy and devoted family. There was obviously some other point to this narrative, but Judith did not wait to discover what it was. She changed channels again, to a natural history film about stick insects. She was alone in the house and allowed herself this first opportunity to cry. She was not crying for her baby or the little girl; she was crying because she felt cheated and blemished. When she realised that her tears were not for her child, or even others like him, but for herself, she stopped. She felt, though she couldn't explain it, that she had denied herself that right.

Patrick saw his mongol in the car. He was pausing at a road junction and glanced up as another car pulled alongside. A mongol man was staring out, not at him, but at the reflection of a Belisha beacon flashing in the wing of Patrick's car. His lips were curled into a small, almost sardonic smile of amusement. When the traffic cleared on the street ahead, both cars pulled off in different directions. Patrick had been shaken by the sight, but less than he had anticipated. He felt he had been expecting to see something like it, and now that the moment had come he was adequately prepared to deal with it. Its inevitability somehow lessened its impact, or this was how he explained it to Judith when he told her about it that evening as they cooked supper. He also told his mother about it on the telephone, and Wanda, over the fence, as he raked up leaves in the garden. One way and another he told a lot of people about it, until eventually he couldn't remember whom he had told and whom he hadn't, so he refrained from mentioning it again, lest he should become a bore. He was, anyway, starting to bore himself.

*　　*　　*

Over breakfast one morning Patrick suggested to Judith that they might visit Essex that coming weekend. It would give his parents the opportunity to see how well they were managing, he said, they would feel more secure on their home ground than in London. 'They are at that age,' he reminded Judith, 'when such things can affect

them.' It was the first time that Patrick had so unequivo-
cally broached the subject of his parents' absence and also
the first time he had, of his own volition, suggested going
out anywhere. It was for this latter reason that Judith
curbed her irritation and agreed.

They set off to Essex on the Friday night after Patrick's
return from work, Patrick's parents stood on the front
porch to meet them, blinking in the evening sunlight.
They exchanged grave, strained embraces, and were led
to the sitting room where sherry was waiting. Patrick's
father was quiet, his expression set and concerned. It was
he who spoke of the baby first. He was relieved he said,
to hear the news of the blood tests and agreed with
Cynthia that the sooner they had another child the sooner
they could put the whole thing behind them. After this
the tension eased and they talked more freely. Over
dinner Patrick and his father discussed Patrick's work
prospects. His mother talked also, of their decision to get
a part-time gardener and the complex difficulties this was
posing in finding anyone suitable. Looking around the
table at their gentle, animated faces Judith felt her own
sense of contentment returning, which surprised her for
she had been convinced she would feel the opposite. The
ritual of dinner was the same as it had always been. The
polished table, adorned with the heavy, glittering cutlery,
the heated trolley standing behind Patrick's mother ready
for second servings, the leisurely progress through the
various courses, the withdrawal into the sitting room for
brandy and coffee.

Judith found herself wondering, as she had often done,
how they ate when they were alone. She tried to picture
them at the gleaming table, with their serviettes and
freshly baked bread rolls, and then realised that they
probably ate in the kitchen when they had no company.
The dining room, now she came to look at it, was clearly
unused. This was not in the sense that her mother's dining

room was unused, it was not dusty and tarnished by neglect, it had a lustre about it, a sparkle, which was almost sacred. The idea of the room, shuttered and entombed and only revealed when the presence of others demanded it, now struck her as depressing. Afraid that her face might betray this, she stooped over her plate and focused her attention on eating.

After dinner Patrick and his father declined the coffee and brandy and decided instead to go the pub. Within moments of their departure Patrick's mother put her arms around Judith and kissed her, telling her what a good and brave girl she had been, and how proud of her she was. Judith was a good deal taller than Patrick's mother and so felt faintly absurd, holding the small, bulky frame against herself. The roots of Patrick's mother's hair were white, sharply changing into a dull, gun-metal grey. Looking down on them Judith realised that her mother-in-law dyed her hair, and tightened her grip on her. She was touched by deep regret at the uncharitable thoughts she had harboured in the past weeks, though why the sight of the whitened roots should trigger this regret she did not know. They washed up and made coffee and sat drinking it in the sitting room. Judith talked about the baby but edited out any details she thought might be too distressing or incomprehensible. Patrick's mother listened, moist-eyed, from the depths of her armchair. She asked at one point what the baby had looked like and Judith briefly described him. She chose her adjectives cautiously, careful not to overemphasise the perfection of his features lest that too should be distressing. She assumed also that if she painted too poignant and pretty a picture of the baby her actions might appear unacceptably callous. But after a while she realised she was worrying needlessly. There was no hint of ambiguity or criticism in Patrick's mother. She did not even appear relieved at their decision. The thought that they would keep the baby had quite obviously never occurred to her.

Patrick and his father walked to the pub which was only half a mile down the road. There was no pavement, and they walked in the breast of the road itself, occasionally pulling in to the side when a car passed. It was dark now, and Patrick's father carried a flashlight, casting its beam over hedgerows, gesturing to the silhouettes of neighbouring houses, filling Patrick in on anecdotes of new inhabitants and local intrigue. They walked slowly, their conversation fluid and relaxed. They rounded a corner to see the lighted windows of the pub and a small armada of cars parked outside. Drifting through the night air they could hear the sound of voices, ribald and laughing. Patrick felt a small ripple of anxiety; he would probably know most of the people in the pub, and in all probability they would also know about the baby, for such things are not easily contained in a small village. His father, as if reading his mind, paused, causing Patrick to halt and glance back at him.

'By the way, we didn't tell anyone about his condition. We simply said he was stillborn.'

Patrick looked at his father's face but it was too dark to decipher his expression. He caught only a vague impression of his features, of his eyes, small and lidded in the distant lights from the pub.

'It saves a lot of explanations, doesn't it? A lot of embarrassment on both sides.'

'If you say so.'

This sounded resentful and Patrick quickly amended it.

'I just think it's unnecessary. These things happen. People have to accept it.'

'Yes, well, I was primarily thinking of you.'

There was a stiffness in his father's voice now; the

flashlight in his hand was cast downwards, splashing a trembling pool of light over their feet.

'We can always drink at home if you prefer.'

'No, no. Now we're here we may as well go in.'

'It simply seemed for the best.'

'Yes, quite. It's a good idea. Thank you.'

Once inside the pub they were greeted by a sea of warm smiling faces. Drinks were ordered and bar stools politely vacated. One or two people clasped Patrick by the hand, and muttered that they knew something of what he must feel. He must regard it as a chapter closed, they said. Someone suggested a game of darts and Patrick and his father were seconded to play. The game was boisterous and argumentative. It continued until after closing time, when Patrick and his father walked home, singing an old boating song, their arms intertwined.

Patrick woke up later that night with a raging headache. Judith was asleep next to him, so he inched cautiously out of the bed so as not to rouse her. In the kitchen he took a couple of aspirins and made himself some cocoa. He drank it leaning against the sink. The kitchen had been repainted since they had last visited and he wasn't sure he approved of the colour, which was shell pink. His parents had never been very tasteful in their choice of wall coverings, and he wished they would consult him before making such decisions. And then he thought, Why should they? He wished in turn that his father had not told everyone the baby was stillborn: it seemed to him now grotesque, and he was filled with revulsion that he had gone along with it. He felt at that moment a surge of paternal loyalty towards the child, mingled with a mounting vindictiveness which was directed towards his father. The power of this disturbed him. He tried to put himself in his father's position, and reasoned that it was a natural enough thing to do. Thinking this, he drank down the cocoa, but too quickly, so that it scalded the inside of his mouth. He rinsed the cup, left it to drain and went back upstairs. As he climbed into bed, Judith woke, and he whispered to her that they must think up some excuse so that they could cut the weekend short and return to London early.

Chapter Eighteen

During the course of the next few weeks more neighbours gradually started to call. They were hesitant initially, and came without their children, but Judith quickly assured them that this was quite unnecessary. She was taken at her word; the neighbours, young women like herself, took to dropping in with their children on the way back from the supermarket or playgroup. Judith and the mothers would sit drinking coffee in the garden, while the children tottered and scampered about them. Judith found herself observing the children more closely, with a new and rather urgent curiosity. They would clamber on to her lap, sticky with chocolate, and she would marvel at the softness of their skins, at the baby plumpness of their wrists and the tireless motion of their small energetic bodies. She watched them with their mothers also, tearful and fretful and writhing in rage. She did this wistfully, conscious that it was a self-indulgence but regarding it also as a form of self-retribution. When the children were gone she collected up the shreds of torn paper and upturned chairs and scattered buttons and gave her emotions full rein. It was these small penances, and others like them, which got her through the day.

Because Judith and Patrick had shown no reluctance to discuss the baby with their friends, their friends continued to reciprocate by talking about the baby whenever they felt inclined to do so. By now Judith and Patrick felt there was no part of the subject which hadn't been analysed and dissected and dismembered. Yet an insatiable, if dispassionate, curiosity persisted about the whole event which they, by their initial encouragement to allow others to dwell upon it, had unwittingly sponsored. They sat at their dinner table ensnared in conversations about medical and moral ethics, and how these differed when applied to a mental as against a physical handicap, and became aware of a new curiosity within themselves.

Both of them, quite independently, began to wonder what their child looked like. They did not voice this to each other, for they were too afraid of its implications; and the very simplicity of the thought gave it a strength which made increased their fear. They found themselves speculating whether or not it was possible for a mongol to inherit some recognisable traits from his parents; whether or not, for example, their son had Patrick's hair colouring or Judith's eyes. Patrick himself started to entertain vague and fantastic notions about anonymously visiting the baby. He imagined some infant nursery, and himself, posing as a prospective adoptive parent, being escorted round and seeing his son sitting astride a push-car amongst all the other children. He imagined squatting by the child, who in his imaginings was aged about two, and talking to him about the car and the child, perfectly articulately, but still quite definitely mongoloid, answering him. He would think these things at his desk at the office, or in the car, or in the bath. The thought itself was disturbing enough, but less so than the ease with which his mind could gravitate towards it.

Judith was aware of the same curiosity but was more adept at controlling it. When she did happen to think of it, the child was usually aged about eleven, wearing a grey, hand-knitted V-neck sweater and bulky grey, knee-length shorts. He always had dark hair and always stood alone. She was never able to place his surroundings and, unlike Patrick, she never approached him. He simply stood, brooding and pug-nosed, on the edge of her consciousness; she allowed him no more access than that.

One day the social workers' department rang from the local authority to confirm details of their ages and address and to tell them that a means test form was being despatched to them; they would be expected to make a regular financial contribution to the upkeep of the child, which could either be paid by a monthly direct debit through their bank account or by a giro-cheque.

On the Friday afternoon Judith took down the sitting room curtains to wash. She had decided to wash all the curtains in the house and this was the first pair she was tackling. She was just unhooking them when she caught sight of a woman pushing open the garden gate. She was in her fifties, dressed in a belted mackintosh and walking shoes; she had a spry, vigorous look to her; under one arm she carried a flat leather document case. She rang the doorbell with a short, crisp ring, and when Judith answered, briskly introduced herself. She was, she said, the local authority social worker, and she would be handling their case from now on.

Although Judith suggested it, she did not sit in the sitting room, as her predecessors had done, but followed Judith into the kitchen and sat at the table watching as Judith made a pot of tea. She talked about the neighbourhood and its rising population of unemployed and the problems this posed for her department, and Judith felt her guard lowering, and them promptly felt wary, wondering if this was the intention. She poured the tea and sat down opposite the woman, who had unzipped her briefcase and was busily consulting some papers. Judith watched her without speaking, preparing herself for the

144

by now familiar pattern of questions, and was disconcerted when the woman stacked up the forms and folded
her hands over them.

'Now,' she said, 'don't go running away with the idea
that because I'm unmarried and have no children that I
don't know what you're going through. I've as good an
idea as the next person, with or without the benefit of
clergy or children.'

She smiled as she said this, undiscouraged that Judith
did not reciprocate.

'Since you've made your decision, I'm quite sure you
don't want to go over it all again, do you?'

Judith shook her head. She was watching the woman
closely, her guard raised once more in case this was some
new untried tactic. The woman's face was narrow and
pointed, sharply divided by a long, thin nose, underneath
which was a generous mouth with a ponderous lower lip.
It was quite the plainest face Judith had ever seen. She
imagined the woman shopping on her way home from
work, buying a frozen lamb chop and a tin of peas and
exchanging mildly risqué jokes with the shopkeeper. She
imagined her in a flat, plain and sensible like herself, with
pictures of her nephews and nieces on the mantelpiece
and a single bed with a Teasmade next to it. It comforted
her to picture these things, to place the woman in a
context in her mind. But the woman was shuffling the
forms again, peering at each one almost impatiently.

'Damn wretched things,' she said, and she spoke as if
she considered herself to be alone and unobserved. She
finally extracted a form and took out a pen.

'Now, I expect you don't want to be troubled by us
needing consent every time he has to have a jab or a
booster shot or whatever, and this will release you of that
burden and let me take it for you.'

Judith hesitated before reaching for the form, and the
woman glanced at her quickly.

'It's more of a convenience for us, Mrs Fielding. You're not the only one who'll gain by it.'

Judith said nothing and the woman went back to the form.

'Both you and your husband should sign so I'll leave it with you, all right? Now, what's next?'

She delved into the pile of papers again and pulled out another one.

'This one's a similar sort of thing, but more relating to his care, so you won't have us pestering you every time he has to be transferred to a foster home or a nursery.'

This form was placed on top of the first one. Judith stared at them uneasily. The woman seemed to sense this, for she said: 'It's quite routine for us to handle these decisions on your behalf, Mrs Fielding. There's nothing to feel anxious about.'

'If you say so.'

'I do.'

A ruled exercise book was now pulled out of the briefcase and flapped open.

'What else . . . ? Ah yes. Some practical questions if you can stand it. Firstly, how do you feel about the baby being adopted?'

Judith was too startled to reply immediately. She fiddled with the corner of one of the forms, creasing it into a small triangle with her fingernails.

'Would anyone really want to adopt him?'

'There are associations, agencies, which cater for finding homes for handicapped children.'

'I see.'

'Would you like me to contact them, see what I can do?'

Judith nodded. The whole idea seemed both incomprehensible and astounding to her, and she thought, But what woman would *choose* to take on such a child which isn't even hers? And then she ducked her head, for the thought of it disturbed her. The social worker said: 'People want children for all sorts of reasons, don't they?'

Judith toyed with the triangle of paper a moment.

'They must be extraordinarily unselfish.'

'Or be extraordinarily confident in their capacity to cope.'

'They're still extraordinary though, aren't they?' Judith replied. 'However you look at it.'

She didn't know why she felt obliged to defend such women, yet she did. The social worker had not finished.

'All right. They deserve our praise and our respect. Everything that's going, in fact. Which doesn't necessarily mean that someone in your position deserves condemnation, does it?'

'I suppose not.'

'Unless of course you feel you have to seek it out.'

Judith glanced up sharply.

'I'd only do that if I regretted what I've done, and I don't.'

'I'm glad to hear it.'

'I really mean it, I don't.'

'And I really believe you, Mrs Fielding, but sometimes experiencing a total lack of regret can promote more guilt than the original event.'

'I'm sorry, I don't understand.'

'Suppose someone dies. Someone close to you. Your mother, for example. And supposing, for various reasons, her death meant very little to you. So you feel no real sense of loss. Supposing then you feel guilty, not because of her death, but because you feel nothing and you think you should. Because she's your mother and society says we should love our mothers, just as everyone says we should love our children. Regardless of what they're like.'

Judith said nothing; she was looking at the woman's hands, lying on the table between them, square and solid and practical. There was no hint of judgement either in her tone or her words, simply an incisive directness, an exactness, which made Judith feel her old sense of confusion returning. The woman was smiling at her in a friendly sort of way, waiting for her to speak.

'I don't know what you expect me to say.'

'Nothing at all. I'm simply thinking out loud. In case you feel like doing the same.'

'If he'd been a girl I'd feel guilt, I'm sure.' Judith said suddenly. 'Or regret. *Something* at least, I know I would.'

She closed her mouth quickly. She had not intended to say this. Under the table she pinched her arms to remind herself to keep up her guard. She was allowing the social worker to draw her out. But this thought was checked by another – that she wanted to be drawn out, that she had been waiting for just this opportunity.

'You wanted a girl, did you?'

'Yes.' This was barely more than a whisper.

'Were you very disappointed it wasn't?'

'Yes.'

'And you were told the day after his birth?'

'Yes.'

'Had you got over your disappointment by then?'

'No.'

'And you think if it had been a girl, you might have made a different decision?'

'No ... I think it might have been that much harder.'

'In what way?'

Judith gripped her arms in revolt against her thoughts, and heard herself saying:

'I think I would have felt more ... protective. That it was more ... part of me.'

'People are more protective of girls, aren't they? Particularly mothers.'

'I suppose so.'

'I'm sure you've experienced that with your own mother.'

Judith thought of Cynthia and did not reply. The woman was watching her, her pointed chin resting in one hand.

'I'd love to do a study of it one day. I really would.'

Judith realised the woman wasn't watching her, she was gazing into the space behind her, lost in thought.

'Study what?'

'All these newspaper stories and bits on television one's always seeing, about people who keep Down's children, not just their natural mothers, but foster mothers too. It seems to be so much more often the girls than the boys. Not always, but ... of course, it's usually the mother's choice. Perhaps the sexuality thing is more complex if it's a son. The identification is that much less. It would be interesting to find out if it's got anything to do with it, wouldn't it?'

Judith felt too tired suddenly to comprehend what was being said to her. She stared at the stack of forms on the table. What does it matter, she thought, it all comes down to a piece of paper in the end. She stood up quickly, clattering with the tea cups.

'I'm taking up your time, I'm sorry.'

The woman was looking at her, her brow puckered anxiously.

'But there is just one other thing I'd like to discuss with you,' she said. 'About his heart.'

Judith stood quite still, a cup in each hand.

'What about it?'

'The doctor thinks there's a chance, just a chance, that he'll need an operation. When he's a little older, in about a year. It's very common apparently.'

Judith set the cups down and wiped her hands on her skirt.

'And you want our permission?'

'We might do, when the time comes. But in the meantime there's something else you should consider. Apparently he's not that strong. If he gets a cold it could well turn into pneumonia and . . . '

Her voice trailed off. Judith stood quite motionless.

'Yes?'

'It would be helpful for us to know, in the event he did get poorly, how you feel about non-preventive medical care?'

It took Judith a moment to apprehend the meaning of the words, and when she did, she spoke immediately, without hesitation.

'I think there are cases when it's entirely appropriate.'

'And in this particular case?'

Judith stared at her, her fist clenched.

'If the situation should occur, Mrs Fielding . . . it would be helpful to know your position . . . '

Once again her voice wavered and in the silence she left Judith felt her thoughts gather.

'You can tell anyone who needs to know that if he dies they won't get sued.'

'Rather a negative way of putting it, isn't it?'

'No more so than non-preventive care, I would have thought. It's just syntax in the end, however you look at it.'

'It's simply something that might come up, Mrs Fielding, during the next few months. He'll be under the care of various doctors, who will all have various ideas on the subject, as you can imagine.'

'As you see, I have just the one.'

'Are you and your husband quite in accord about it?'

'Yes.'

'You're sure?'

'Oh don't worry. I speak for us both.'

The woman flashed her a look; it seemed for a moment she was about to comment, but she refrained. Instead she said: 'Right, well that's clear enough.'

The zip was pulled on the document case, and then quickly opened again.

'Oh, yes, there is just one last thing. This relates to when he gets older. In case he wants to know details about you and your husband. What would you like us to tell him?'

'What kind of details?'

'Hobbies, interests. You know, the sort of thing children ask.'

Judith opened her mouth and closed it and thought, And what do you tell him if he asks why we didn't want him? Aloud, she said: 'My husband plays football. Neither of us are very musical although we enjoy listening to it. We read a lot and go to the cinema. Is that enough?'

'I'm sure it is, thank you.'

She pencilled these details into a notebook and slapped it closed, sliding it into the document case.

'Well, I shall handle everything I can from now on, Mrs Fielding. I'll try not to disturb you unless it's absolutely necessary. Just post the forms back to me, will you?'

'Is that it?'

The woman smiled, her plain face momentarily illuminated by something like prettiness.

'That's it. Now you can get on with the rest of your life.'

Judith saw another flash of the wide, generous mouth curving into a smile before the woman marched off towards the front door. Judith stood watching her walk down the street, briefcase under one arm, the other one swinging almost military style, the belted mackintosh flapping in the breeze, as the brogue walking shoes propelled her around the corner and out of sight.

Chapter Nineteen

They went back to the hospital for genetic counselling about two weeks later. They sat in front of a young man in a white coat. Behind him was a chart of symbols which Judith took to be chromosomes and she looked at them and thought, So those are the little buggers. They were asked questions about themselves and whether or not there were any other mongols in the family and the young man pulled out a calculator from a drawer and pushed the buttons and then told them that he'd place the chances of it recurring, assuming they had other children relatively quickly, at one in one hundred and fifty. This ratio, he informed them, would increase with their age, and if they delayed having a child, he would advise further counselling. He described to them the test for which Judith would be eligible in any further pregnancies and put his calculator back into the drawer. The interview took less than eleven minutes.

A few days later Patrick's firm asked him to go up to Leeds for two days, on a business trip. He told Judith and they agreed the trip might alleviate his agorophobia, which is what they now called it, and Patrick left on the Friday morning. Apart from his journeys to work and the weekend they had spent at his parents, it was the first time he had been away from home since the baby's birth.

On the Friday afternoon, Chris telephoned to invite them to a party. When she told him she was alone, he said he would be delighted to take her along anyway. He arranged to pick her up at eight-thirty.

She spent the rest of the afternoon preparing herself. She had stopped bleeding by now, but through habit she took a salt bath, and washed her hair and put it in heated rollers. Most of her clothes were too large for her and she was considering going out to buy something new when she came across an old dress she had bought with her first wage packet as an infant teacher. It was black, simply but still fashionably cut, with a dramatic low cut neckline. She put it on and was amazed at the transformation. She barely recognised herself. She looked young and pretty and feminine. She felt, regarding her reflection in her bedroom mirror, like an imposter, and the idea of this excited her.

At eight o'clock she sat in the living room, drinking a gin, waiting for Chris. She fell to imagining herself living alone, unmarried and childless, waiting for a young man to take her to a party, and wondered why she'd never missed experiencing this before. Occasionally she rose to check the time on the clock on the cooker and once again the image of herself reflected in its chrome surface excited her. Chris arrived punctually at eight-thirty and she could see by his expression that he was impressed and even a little startled by her appearance. He offered her his arm and in the car was unusually constrained with her.

The party was in North London. It was confined to two crowded downstairs rooms, swarming with expensive and exotically dressed people she did not know. Chris guided her amongst them and she stood on the edges of conversations, listening and smiling and quite at ease. A little later Chris asked her to dance and then another man approached her. She caught sight of herself in a mirror, her face flushed and glowing, raised attentively to her partner, his arm about her, and still she did not recognise herself. People asked her what she did and she found herself saying that she was a teacher and did not amend it to the past tense. There was a buffet meal of rice and cold meat and a young man served her, and then promptly sat next to her on the sofa, talking about a film he'd recently seen and the thought entered her head that he was talking to her as he might talk to any pretty girl at a party. In this respect he thought her entirely ordinary and this pleased her. She looked down at her hands, resting beside the plate of food on her lap, and tried to remember them holding the baby and signing the care order forms, and failed, and this too pleased her.

Later she left the young man to go into the other room, where another young man asked her to dance; she remembered other parties, years before, when she would sit in a corner watching a girl like herself being surrounded by men and feel envious, and she wondered, looking up at the smooth-faced young man who now held her, why it had meant so much, and why it meant so little now. Yet she knew herself to be happy. After a while she stopped puzzling over it and allowed herself to be caught up in the moment. She danced almost continuously for nearly two hours, mostly with different partners, who materialised as soon as the music paused. Eventually she found herself being held by Chris. He was looking at her in a way she had not seen before, and holding her quite differently from the way he had when they had last danced in the Essex back garden. After a while he took her hand and she let him lead her outside. They sat on a low wall behind the house, where he lit a cigarette. She glanced at his face, but still could not assess his expression. They sat silently for a while until he said:

'I often think, you know, about what I said to you in the hospital that day.'

'About what?'

'The baby. How he would change you. I feel badly about it sometimes. Things turning out as they have.'

'Forget it. I have.'

He said nothing to this, but said instead:

'But you have changed, all the same . . . as if I've never seen you before.'

'Why, for heaven's sake?'

'Perhaps I never looked closely enough, I don't know.'

He sounded genuinely puzzled and she glanced at him again.

'You've certainly had ample opportunity.'

'Yes, I know.'

He didn't speak for a moment, then he said:

'I admire you very much, you know that, don't you?'

'Don't be absurd.'

'It's the truth.'

He said it vehemently, and she recoiled slightly, without knowing why.

'I admire what you've done. Or rather the way you've done it. The way you've never asked for pity or cared what people say about you. How you've never doubted it . . . all of it.'

'Well there's nothing to admire about it, I assure you.'

She spoke roughly and this seemed to trouble him.

'Anyway, most people say what we've done is right. They go to great pains to tell us that. In fact sometimes I'd rather like to hear a voice raised in dissent.'

'Why?'

'Because I've never been required to defend it. Except to the social workers. And I'd like to.'

'You think you need to?'

'Not at all. I'd just like to hear myself doing it. It all gets so terribly polite, you see.'

He seemed to accept this, or at least not to question it.

'I don't know many women who would have done it. That's all I'm saying.'

'Perhaps you don't know women as well as you think.'

'Perhaps.' He paused, and then said: 'That doesn't necessarily mean I'm wrong about this, though.'

She looked at the lights in the house and the shapes of the people moving within it.

'Other people's problems always seem more dramatic than they really are, don't you think?'

'Why must you be so stoical all the time?'

'I'm not. I'm just not going to accept credit where it's not due. I'm not going to cash in on it.'

'That's just utter nonsense.'

'The only reason you think what I've done is so . . . admirable, is because it's the last thing anyone expected of me. You said that yourself. Good old Judith stood her ground for once and said no. Well, my mother would say it's rather a shame I left it so late and did it over something so negative.'

'Why d'you say it's negative?'

'Chris, don't make me go over it all again. Please.'

'A moment ago you said you'd like to defend it.'

'But not explain it. I've done that until I'm sick of hearing it.'

'Of course. I'm sorry.'

They sat without speaking a moment, then he suddenly said in a different tone:

'I want you, you know that, don't you?'

She stared straight ahead, too stunned to reply. She felt a quick stab of pleasure at the urgency in his voice. She knew she should get up and go back inside the house, but she didn't move.

'But there's Patrick, of course. He's my friend. It would be unforgivable.'

She was irritated by this and realised she had not

thought of Patrick all evening. It seemed an irrelevance
to bring him up now, although that too was something
she could not explain. She was aware of Chris gazing at
her steadily, and of her own disinclination to look at him.
She pressed her fingers into the nobbled, powdery surface
of the wall and said nothing.

'It's very complicated, isn't it?'

She nodded, without speaking and uncertain even if she
agreed. She was buying time now to adjust to this new
turn of events. She was afraid he might touch her.

'Come.'

She felt his hand on her arm, and allowed herself to be
steered around a gravel path to the front of the house. He
led her to his car, parked in the driveway under some
trees. She wondered if he'd parked there deliberately and
then decided she was probably being hard on him. He
fumbled for his keys and she got a look at his face: intense
and curiously bitter. Inside the car he stubbed out his
cigarette and reached for her, his hands, dry and
quivering, brushing over her breasts and arms. He kissed
her and his mouth was hot, his breath coming in short,
hard bursts. She caught a glimpse of his dark, intelligent
eyes, hooded and detached, staring down at her bare
shoulders and chest. His hand was moving inside the
front of her dress, his fingers reaching for her nipple, and
all at once she remembered the touch of the baby's
tongue, flicking over it, and how she had felt, a few hours
before, when the young man was talking to her on the
sofa, and her pleasure in the realisation that he thought
her ordinary; and she thought now of Chris's sudden
pleasure in the fact that she wasn't, and then she knew
what she had to do.

'Don't,' she said, and her tone was that of a reproving
nurse and he accepted the authority in it instantly, as she
had known he would. She got out of the car and returned
to the house, where she found the young man, still on the

sofa, gloomily drinking, and quite unabashed she asked him to dance. Later he drove her to his flat where they romped on his unmade bed and giggled while he scoured the room for a Durex and giggled again over his collection of old records; at dawn he rang for a taxi and she went home. Sitting in the taxi she felt tousled and faintly ridiculous, but oddly exhilarated. The young man did not ask to see her again, and she did not encourage him to. She could not remember if he'd told her his name.

That evening Patrick returned from Leeds and she told him Chris had taken her to a party, that she had known nobody there, but that it had made a pleasant change. Patrick told her he too had been out while in Leeds, he and a client had spent the night hitting the high spots. It had been tiring, he said, but that it had also made a pleasant change.

*   *   *

For the first time in more years than she cared to remember, Cynthia bought herself a dress. She bought it in a boutique in a West End department store; she did not try it on for she could not face the prospect of denuding herself in a communal changing room crowded with teenage girls, but when she tried it on at home she was pleasantly surprised. It was soft, pale green cotton, pleated, with a high neck, and altogether it lent her a dignified sober appearance which she decided was entirely appropriate.

Richard, her solicitor friend, was calling in to see her that evening to discuss the baby, and she was anxious to create the right impression. Richard had handled both her divorces, as well as advising her in various other capacities, most notably when she was twice named as co-respondent in other people's divorces; she therefore knew she had to dispel the unfavourable impressions these events had undoubtedly left in his mind.

Chapter Nineteen

After changing, she swept out the sitting room, stuffing the old newspapers and magazines down the sides of the armchairs, battled with the ice tray (for she recollected that he liked ice in his whisky) and arranged flowers in vases she found scattered around the house. She then sat waiting for his arrival with unaccustomed nervousness. He had been almost curt with her on the telephone, insisting that he discuss the situation with her before she took matters further. Although he was several years younger than she, he had always seen her with a kind of worldly bemusement. He would sit at his desk amongst the mountainous litter of her financial and marital documents and plead with her to help him sort them into some kind of order, as if by imposing discipline on the papers he might have some chance to impose discipline on her also. Yet he did this with the air of a man tackling a lost cause, and would eventually concede defeat and stuff the papers back into her file, which he declared was nothing short of a clerical disaster area. However, he was clearly fond of her, and it was on this that she now intended to capitalise.

When he arrived she poured him a whisky and sat him amongst the flowers in the sitting room and arranged herself carefully in a chair opposite him. He had not, she observed, brought her file with him, and she was relieved. Any favourable impression she might make would, she knew, be quickly betrayed by the documented evidence of past misdemeanours. He was nearly bald, although this was ineffectually disguised by a low parting over one ear which enabled several long strands of hair to be combed over the bare dome of his head. Otherwise his features were quite unremarkable. He seemed, initially, to be absorbed in watching the cubes of ice jiggling in his drink, but she knew of old that he was building up to speak. She waited, fingering the pleats of her dress, her legs neatly folded.

'I just want to get one or two things straight,' he said, raising his eyes to her almost reluctantly. 'I feel there are some points which need clarifying.'

'By all means,' and she smiled as she said it, wishing he would hurry his drink so that she had the excuse to replenish her own.

'You are quite resolved that you want the baby?'

'Yes, I thought I'd made that clear.'

'What you haven't made clear is why.'

'I want to provide him with a home, of course.'

'In spite of the stand your daughter has taken, or because of it?'

'Quite obviously if she'd decided to keep him there wouldn't be any need for me to intervene, would there?' She said this airily, and then checked herself, afraid that she might sound flippant.

'What does she feel about your intention?'

'I haven't discussed it with her yet. I wanted to make sure she didn't change her mind first. I did mention it to Patrick, her husband.'

'What did he say?'

'I doubt he took it seriously, any more than you do.'

'If I didn't take it seriously I wouldn't be here now, talking to you.'

'Questioning me is rather more like it.'

'These are only questions others will ask you, Cynthia.'

The use of her name was oddly formal, like a reprimand.

'I'm his grandmother. Have I no rights at all?'

'They might not supersede those of his mother.'

'Even if she's rejected him?'

'Her feelings will still be taken into account. It's inevitable.'

'That's what the law says, is it?'

'He'll be under what's called a section one care order.

So in that sense, yes, it's what the law says. It's also what the social workers on the case might say. It all depends on their attitude and how they assess yours.'

'Have you spoken to them?'

'No, that's something you'll have to do. But I have made some general enquiries, to find out if what you want is viable.'

'And is it?'

'Legal adoption might prove to be complicated, but not, I suppose, entirely impossible. It's also possible, depending, as I say, on the view of those concerned, that you might be considered in some kind of fostering capacity.'

'Does that mean he can come here to live with me?'

'Theoretically. But there are . . . obstacles. Your age for one thing. The fact that you're single. Not to mention the fact you have two failed marriages behind you.'

'What has that got to do with anything?'

'It'll be regarded as an indication of character, of your ability to handle relationships. Look at it from their viewpoint. A woman in the autumn of her life . . . '

'Spare me the poetry, please.'

'All right. However you care to wrap it up, a woman in her middle age suddenly wants to take on a mentally retarded child with all the demands that implies. They'll naturally want to look at these things in perspective, won't they? See how you've fared in your other relationships, if nothing else to see that you've got the stamina.'

'In other words I'm done for before I begin.'

'Not at all. But these are aspects they'll want to cover. I want you to know what you could be stirring up.'

'You're not trying to frighten me off by any chance?'

'I think I know you rather better than that.'

He smiled at her, almost ruefully, and swallowed some of the whisky. Then he said: 'The main problem will be

Judith. If she opposes you, which she might well do, it will damage your chances considerably. The only factor that can possibly go in your favour is what the prospects are for the child himself.'

'In what sense?'

'If it seems likely he'll spend his life in some institution, then your application will be very sympathetically considered.'

'In spite of Judith?'

'If they were thoroughly satisfied you could provide the sort of care he requires . . . put it this way, it might redress the balance between you.'

'Balance?'

'Between your respective rights over the child.'

This seemed to satisfy Cynthia, and she lit a cigarette. He watched her over the rim of his glass before speaking.

'I told you about my brother's child, didn't I?'

'Yes.'

'As I say, I'm very fond of him. Very. But then of course I only see him when I'm visiting a few times a year. Christmas and that kind of thing.'

'So?'

'So, I wouldn't like to think anything I've said . . . has influenced you in any way.'

'Oh no. I thought it up entirely on my own. Your hands are quite clean.'

He stared at her, surprised and then bewildered at her choice of words.

'I only meant it's not going to be easy.'

'I never imagined it would be.'

'And when your daughter does discover what you plan on doing, that might not be easy either.'

She said nothing to this.

'I mean, in God's name, Cynthia, how will you ever explain it to her? How?'

'I'll just have to find a way.'

'Forgive me, but you haven't explained it to me. Not adequately.'

'Have I not?'

'Beyond saying that you want him, no.'

She inhaled sharply on her cigarette before replying.

'Presumably this will be another question I'll be asked by the social workers?'

'The first, I imagine.'

'Well, I shall just have to make sure I'm word perfect when it comes to answering it, won't I? Let me top up your glass.'

With this she rose and swiftly took his glass to fill it with whisky. Then she asked him to come and give her some advice on the garden; being a man, she said, he knew so much more about these things than she did. They stood on the verandah and talked about bi-annuals and the best time to put out bedding plants and, after refusing a third drink, he left. It was only when he was in his car that he realised she had never answered his question.

Chapter Twenty

Patrick's stress symptoms were easing almost daily. He no longer felt the need to take either his Valium or his sleeping pills so regularly. One night he swept home from work in a state of excitement, but one quite unlike his former agitation. Judith was peeling potatoes in the kitchen and he stood behind her, breathless and slightly triumphant.

'I've just seen the most fantastic house.'

She turned to look at him, her hands covered in scales of potato peelings.

'What house?'

'A block or so away from the office, just come on the market. Same period as this. Been split up into flats. Needs a bit of work, of course, but nothing we can't handle, I'm sure.'

He pulled off his jacket as he spoke, with the air of a man getting to grips with something.

'Even got a garden, nothing much, but not bad for central London. You wait 'til you see it. You'll love it, love it.'

He grinned at her almost boyishly, but anxiously, needing her approval.

'But we don't need to move. We only got this place straight a few months ago.'

'So we'll be that much more expert, won't we? You can do all the decor, like before. I leave it all to you. We'll just strip off everything that's there and start from scratch.'

Judith looked down at the potatoes bobbing about in the discoloured water in the washing-up bowl. A terrible tiredness descended on her. She saw herself organising an armoury of builders and electricians and enthusing over shades of wallpaper and carpets, and her fatigue increased at the thought.

'Can we afford it? We've got a big enough mortgage as it is. And what about the upkeep of the baby, we've got that to consider.'

'People move house even with children at home, don't they? Don't bring that up as an excuse.'

He felt cheated by her lack of response, and showed it, but then his manner suddenly softened, and he placed his hands on her shoulders so that she was facing him again.

'This is just what we need, don't you see? Something

we can tackle together. God knows you've got to do something with your time. Sooner or later you're going to run out of cupboards to clean and curtains to wash, and then what?'

She said nothing and he took this to mean a tacit acceptance of his words.

'We can make a flat of the upstairs rooms while the rest's being done up. There's bags of room. And we'll get cracking on another baby. It's a great house for a kid, you wait and see.'

He was waiting for her to reply now, but she did not. She felt she was choking, and the image of herself holding and suckling another baby aggravated the sensation. He relinquished his grasp on her shoulders in a gesture of despair.

'I thought you'd jump at the chance. I thought you'd be overjoyed.'

'I haven't said anything against it, have I?' She said this uneasily, guiltily.

'I suppose it's because I've suggested it,' he said, ignoring her last words. 'Because it's come from me. And of course you're the only one allowed to make decisions aren't you? As you've proved.'

He seemed shocked he had said it, or at any rate surprised. She was looking at him but he did not meet her eyes. She felt as if the walls of the kitchen were closing in on her. She was determined not to rise to his words, not because she was frightened of their significance, but because she felt them to be so appallingly predictable. The night after the party, Patrick's undisclosed sojourn in Leeds, their polite remoteness with each other – it was all like a predestined pattern. They had felt no guilt so they had tried to create it in another form. And now, having failed, it seemed they were to turn against each other and that too seemed predictable.

Patrick's suggestion that they should move also fell, it

seemed to her, into this category. She could hear the response of their friends, endorsing the wisdom of his inspiration. 'A fresh start' and 'Now you can put the whole thing behind you.' She closed her eyes in concentration, as if wishing their words into her mind, but all she could see was the grey V-necked pullover and the brooding, pug-nosed face, and even the vision of that seemed a dismal banality. She was amazed at her cynicism and her detachedness, and a little alarmed by it. Patrick was talking again, about the house and the room dimensions, and she tried to listen, wondering if she could ever articulate her thoughts to him. He looked much as he had at the hospital immediately after the birth of the baby, buoyant and animated, and she knew he would look that way increasingly now, for he had clearly resolved to, and this thought made her feel unbearably tired also.

She sank into a chair as he continued to speak. He had worked it all out. They would put their own house on the market and increase their mortgage and get a bank loan to cover any outstanding balance. Within a year he would be made an associate partner in the practice so providing for another child would be no problem. They must regard the maintenance of the first as part of their general domestic outgoings. She listened in silence as he sketched out their future, which encouraged him to assume her acquiescence, which was her intention. Later they had supper and watched television and went to bed, where Patrick announced his intention to stop taking his Valium and sleeping pills. They had served their purpose, he said. She offered to flush them down the lavatory, but outside the bedroom door she put them in the frilled pocket of her gingham dressing gown. She would transfer them to her handbag in the morning.

*   *   *

Patrick found it difficult to sleep. He tossed restlessly for a while, and then resigned himself to wakefulness and lay, looking down at Judith sleeping beside him. Her face looked strained, even in repose, her mouth compressed into a thin, tight line of determination. The lost weight, he now thought, did not suit her. Her cheeks were too hollow, her jaw bone too pronounced; there was altogether a severity about her face which unsettled him, yet this was mixed with a profound protectiveness, which troubled him equally for he knew it was beyond his capability to express it.

His thoughts turned to his overnight stay in Leeds and he wondered why he had found it necessary to lie about it. He had spent the day with a client, who had suggested, as their business drew to a close, a night out at the various clubs he knew. He was a plump, florid little man with a mottled complexion and a nose which alternated between shades of light crimson and mauve. When he had made his suggestion he had nudged Patrick in the ribs, and laughed in a throaty kind of way. Patrick disliked this kind of familiarity and the triteness of the innuendo which accompanied it. He politely excused himself on the grounds of a prior appointment, and took a taxi to visit a married couple he had known at university.

They lived on the outskirts of Leeds, in a tiny, redbrick Victorian terraced house, with deceptively austere overtones. He was greeted at the front door by Liz, whom he hadn't seen for over five years. She was wearing a man's sweater with the sleeves rolled up, and a pair of patched denim jeans. Her hands were covered with flour. Her hair, which had once been red and long and plentiful, was cut short, and sprinkled with grey. She was fatter than he remembered, but he thought she looked marvellous. She flung her arms around him joyously, and he picked his way through a narrow hall filled with bicycles and prams and into a kitchen which was overrun with children.

Mistaking his expression, she hastily explained that only three of them were hers, and accordingly three of the infants were plucked off the floor and from beneath the table to be introduced. The kitchen was small and totally devastated. Toys and nappy pails and unwashed plates and tubs of powder paint lacking lids were indiscriminately littered over every surface. In a corner, a washing machine noisily gurgled under the din of the shrieking children and a record player in a cupboard mercilessly intoned nursery rhymes at the wrong speed. In the middle of it all stood Liz, hands immersed in a bowl of flour and eggs, shouting at him to pull up a chair and get himself a glass of wine. The children themselves – he counted six in all – were in various stages of undress, and were aged between one and seven and clambered about on whatever furniture was still upright.

His initial instinct was to turn tail and run, but gradually, as his ears got accustomed to the racket and the wine took its effect (it was home-made and surprisingly potent), he allowed himself to become submerged in the chaos and even began to enjoy it. A while later a rather brisk, talkative woman called round and three of the children were reluctantly carted off and the decibel level dropped fractionally and he and Liz were able to exchange snatches of news. He did not tell her about the baby, for it was not appropriate at that moment, and this both liberated and relaxed him, though he put it down to the effects of the wine.

Nick, her husband, also an engineer, was not due home until later, and Patrick was marshalled into assisting with the ritual of bedtime. He bathed the children and read to them and conducted protracted and alarmingly sophisti-cated negotiations over whether or not night lights were adequate in wattage to ward off ghosts and why it was necessary to brush one's teeth in a vertical as well as a horizontal direction, and at eight o'clock collapsed into

an armchair in a state of nervous but quite euphoric
exhaustion.

When Nick came home they decanted another bottle
of the wine and Liz defrosted something which he took
to be stew and they regaled each other with stories about
university and the antics of mutual friends. All in all it was
a splendid evening. He still did not mention the baby for
it still seemed inappropriate, and he was anyway anxious
not to disturb such a conducive and pleasant atmosphere.

It was decided he should spend the night and a nylon
sleeping bag was laid out on a layer of cushions from the
sofa on the sitting room floor. At two a.m. he stumbled
into the sleeping bag and lay amongst the debris of jigsaw
puzzles and wax crayons and realised he was entirely
happy. He suddenly thought of his own immaculate
house, and for the first time the image of it seemed vapid
and insubstantial. He realised then why it was he had
always considered the Essex house as his home; it had
acquired the memories and associations of his childhood,
whereas the associations of his present house were vague,
and because of recent events, not entirely pleasant. It was
then he resolved that they should move and have another
child. He visualised Judith as Liz had been, crumpled and
maternal, her lost weight regained, up to her elbows in
flour, surrounded by their children, and the vision of this
filled him with a new vigour.

He was woken the next morning by Liz's children
bouncing up and down on his chest, and was relieved that
the idea still seemed entirely viable. As he prepared to
slide out of the sleeping bag, his knee caught something
hard, encrusted on to its inner shiny surface, which he
instantly realised was the result of a wet dream. Still safely
camouflaged inside the bag, he attempted to peel off the
evidence with his fingers, but it refused to budge. He was
tempted to ignore it, but remembered the sleeping bag

belonged to the eldest child, who was seven and showed a quite virulent capacity to ask awkward questions. He therefore stood up, hooked the sleeping bag under each arm, and delighted the children by doing a series of bunny hops to the downstairs cloakroom, where he recalled having seen a wash basin. There was no lock on the door, so he leant against it while the children yelled and battered on the other side, and rubbed the evidence off with the dampened corner of a towel. It did the trick nicely and nylon at least had the advantage of drying quickly.

None of this, of course, explained his disinclination to tell Judith of his visit to Liz and Nick, and looking back on it he could only think it was because he wished to protect her. He knew he could not be dispassionate in his descriptions of the Leeds household, or even why he should be, and he knew that she would contrive to show her usual, stiff indifference, which would irritate him because it always did. Their relationship, he decided, was nevertheless sufficiently strong to withstand such a negligible white lie.

* * *

The following week Judith was surprised by a visit from the local authority social worker. She stood on the doorstep, poised and prim in her belted mackintosh, and said something had come up which she felt she should discuss with Judith, and could she come in for a moment.

Judith led the way into the kitchen, where the woman declined her offer of tea and gestured for Judith to sit at the table opposite her. Judith somewhat apprehensively obeyed, and in the short pause that preceded the woman speaking, her apprehension increased.

'My department has received an enquiry,' she said, 'concerning your son.'

'What kind of enquiry?'

'Initially for fostering, apparently with a view to adoption.'

'But that's marvellous . . . that's wonderful.'

The woman did not reply and Judith frowned at her suspiciously.

'What is it? Is it his health? Isn't he eligible for adoption?'

'That's yet to be determined. In this particular case it isn't really the point.'

'What's the problem then?'

'There may not be one. I didn't handle the enquiry myself. I was simply told about it. It's all at a very preliminary stage.'

'Did they just want any mong . . . Down's baby, or did they ask for mine in particular?'

'Oh quite specifically for yours, Mrs. Fielding.'

'How did they know about him?'

'I assume from you.'

'Me?'

'The enquiry came from your mother.'

Judith stared at her uncomprehendingly. She could feel the blood rush to her face and then drain, as if from every pore in her body.

'You didn't know about it?'

'No, of course not. You're sure it was my mother?'

'Yes. I thought you didn't know. I felt sure you would have mentioned it. I had to find out, you see, at first hand, to see what your reaction was.'

Judith said nothing. She felt the fist inside her clenching once more.

'She didn't mention it at all, not a word?'

Judith shook her head soundlessly. One of Wanda's children was crying in the garden, his scream rising and falling like the crest of a wave.

'Perhaps you'd like to think about it? To discuss it?'

Judith said nothing.

'If you can, I'd like to know your initial reaction, Mrs Fielding. Sometimes they are the most valid. It doesn't mean a commitment or that you can't change your mind. But it might tell us both something of what you really feel about it.'

'Try and say what's in your mind. Whatever it is.'

Judith opened her mouth but no words came out. Her thoughts were so many she felt herself to be drowning in them. She was aghast at their force. All at once she remembered her labour, the black mask of the gas descending, and her humiliating, pathetic cry of 'Mother!' She wondered if after all Cynthia had been in the hospital, and had heard it, and if this was her reply.

Chapter Twenty-One

It was twilight when Judith arrived at Cynthia's house, and drizzling. The house loomed dark and impenetrable above her. There was no answer to her raps on the door, and she sat shivering for a while on the front steps. It occurred to her that Cynthia might be inside the house and refusing to answer the door, but she quickly realised that this was not in character. She was calmer now, and exhausted by her attempts to grapple with her thoughts. After a bit she rose and walked around the house, shielding her eyes, peering into the windows. She could see only her reflection and the familiar darkened contours of the room beyond. The back door was locked and she trudged around to the front again. She knew it could be hours before Cynthia returned, but she knew that she had to wait.

She sat on the steps once more, looking into the street and the houses opposite. They were smaller than she recollected, and better maintained. The street had acquired a new persona over the years since she had left it; carriage lamps now swung from porticos and car ports dominated driveways. Only Cynthia's house was unaltered, with its blistered paintwork and sprawling creeper which tapped on the windows in the breeze.

She remembered other occasions when she had been seated on the same steps – as a child, after school, fingering her chilblains, waiting for Cynthia to return from some unexplained excursion, or simply sitting there to avoid her presence in the house. She recalled these things with a terrible sense of inertia. It seemed apposite that she should find herself seated there once again, and the inevitability of it gave her no comfort.

The drizzle was developing into fine powdery slashes of rain. The trees around the house rustled and trembled as the wind shook them, their leaves breaking loose to spiral and weave to the ground beneath. She stood up once more and shook at the front door. She walked back, around the side of the house, pushing and prising each window as she passed it. Most of the frames were soft and rotting, the wood exposed, the paint hanging in tattered strips. She marvelled, as she always had, at her mother's ability to live alone and untroubled when so inadequately protected. Thinking this, she put her full weight against a window, until she heard the wood splinter like a gunshot as the casement shuddered under the strain, and she was able to ease her arm through the opening between the window joints and release the catch. It only took a second for her to hoist herself on to the sill and she was inside.

She tore her arm in the process, and several angry scratches stood out on the soft inner flesh of her forearm. She bathed it under the kitchen tap, and then went into the sitting room. It was full of wilting, decaying flowers, their fragrance hanging like a vapour over the room. She lay on the sofa for perhaps ten minutes, her body hunched against the cold, her nostrils filled with the scent of the dying flowers, until eventually she fell asleep.

When Cynthia returned, she did not notice the broken and splintered window but went straight into the kitchen to pour herself a drink. She had been to a cinema club where smoking was not permitted and now longed only to relax with a gin and a cigarette. She did not go into the sitting room, but sat in the kitchen, thinking about the film, which had concerned a Vietnam war veteran returning home, when she heard footsteps approaching down the darkened passage. She sat frozen a moment, then cast around for a weapon, but the only thing to hand which was even remotely appropriate was a carving fork. She was just reaching for it when Judith appeared in the doorway.

'My God,' Cynthia said, and laughed out loud, her hand still resting on the table, an inch away from the fork. 'I thought you were a burglar.'

Judith did not reply but simply stood, gazing at her mother's outstretched hand. Cynthia tried and failed to meet her daughter's eyes; in that instant her relief contracted sharply back into fear, and then defiance.

Judith's face was white, even to her lips. She looked almost ghostly under the shadeless glare of the electric light, and Cynthia felt her fear returning.

'I was asleep,' Judith said. She spoke quite calmly, as if she was talking to herself. 'When I woke I didn't know where I was. I thought I was at home in bed, but the walls were too far away and nothing seemed right somehow. Then I heard someone moving about. I waited to feel frightened, but I didn't. And then of course I remembered where I was.'

Cynthia said nothing. She was aware of every muscle in her body, taut as piano wire.

'And I also remembered,' Judith went on in her thin,

tired voice, 'why it was I was here, and all the things I had rehearsed in my mind to say to you, and I knew I couldn't. That it was pointless. You were always so much better at this sort of thing than me.'

'It's hardly a situation we've been in before.'

'Perhaps not, but you wouldn't have created it if you weren't certain you could handle it. Or handle me.'

She said this as an afterthought, but expressionlessly as if the subject no longer interested her.

'So you're not going to fight me?'

'No.'

'You want me to have the child?'

Judith gave a small shrug implying the question was beyond her understanding. Then she said: 'Would you, in my place?'

'Not at first. But when you'd thought it out, I rather hoped you'd see the logic in it.'

Judith smiled at this and said:

'There's never been any logic, Mother, never.'

'There is in that I owe you, wouldn't you say?'

Cynthia said this lightly, hoping she would be contradicted.

'I see. So it's a debt discharged is it? One neglected childhood for another?'

'You know how I hate that sort of melodramatic talk.'

Cynthia turned away to pick up her glass. Her hands were shaking. She wished she'd not opened up this avenue of conversation. A silence fell, they were both waiting for the other to speak.

'I don't know what you expect me to say.' It was Cynthia who spoke first, 'I suppose I knew you would dwell on his childhood as much as you've dwelt on your own. Because it's in your nature. I doubt you can change that any more than I can. All I could hope to do is protect you from it.'

'A little late, isn't it?'

Cynthia smiled rather grimly, as if this was not worthy of an answer.

'I know, too, that you're too decent and good to deny him the chance of a home, even if it's only with me. I was relying on that. I'm still relying on it.'

'I intended to stop you. That's what I came to do.'

'But you've thought better of it, haven't you? You see, I've been very thorough. I've thought it all out, from every point of view. Yours too. Especially yours.'

Cynthia was aware of a tremor in her voice, and paused in an effort to control it.

'You will have to surrender him to me because it's the morally correct thing to do, and you still care about these things, in spite of everything. You'll hate every moment of course, and me, I expect that. But perhaps you'll hate yourself a little less, and I will take him for precisely that reason. So you see, there is a logic.'

Judith said nothing. She could hear her mother talking but her words spun and drifted above her head. She imagined Cynthia as an old woman, white-haired and frail and indomitable, walking down the street, her son shambling along beside her.

'Logical perhaps, but not very practical.'

'Ah, you think I'm not up to it? You assume, I imagine, my failure to meet your demands means I can't possibly hope to meet his?' There was an edge to her voice now, confident that she was on familiar ground. 'Well, my expectations aren't as high as they used to be, which is at least one bonus age brings. Since I expect nothing from him I won't be disappointed, will I? I won't get discouraged. In that respect we should rub along very nicely together.'

'Mother.'

Judith said this in despair and exasperation. She was cowed by the implication of her mother's words, yet quite alienated from them. And she was bitter, bitter that this conversation, like all their conversations, was to be conducted from the armoury of Cynthia's deadly and clinical expertise in these things. There was, she saw, no way through her mother's reasoned and detached countenance. But as she thought this Cynthia suddenly astounded her by starting to sob, her rigid stance abruptly crumbling as she stooped, holding her arm across her stomach as if in pain. Judith watched her, transfixed.

'What are you crying for?'

Cynthia waved the question aside.

'Why the tears, Mother? You're going to get your way, aren't you? It's all working out as you planned.'

Again Cynthia waved the question aside. She moved away, snuffling and shuddering, her back now turned to her daughter.

'You're right,' she said, 'it isn't practical. I'm getting too old for this.' She was silent for a moment, and then she said, almost ruefully, 'I expected you to be the one to cry. I expected rage, I was prepared for that. My God, you say you had it all rehearsed, well so did I. I was ready for anything you could throw at me except your indifference. I never was equipped to deal with that.'

She turned at this point to smile through her tears.

'And I was going to be so convincing. You would have been proud of me. Everyone had to be convinced, particularly you.'

Judith stared at her mother's face, her features stiffened by self-contempt.

'I don't understand.'

'And you never would, so it's hopeless. I knew looking at your face a moment ago it was hopeless. Oh, going through with it, I could do that. That's the easy part. It would be like snuffing out a candle. And since you already despised me, I thought it wouldn't matter. But it does. It does.'

With this she stumbled from the room. Judith stood for some moments, retracing the conversation in her mind and then starting again, and each time the conclusion was the same. She could hear Cynthia's footsteps above her, and the sound of a tap running, then silence. After a few minutes she went to the telephone and rang Patrick to say she would be spending the night with Cynthia.

* * *

A little later Judith made a hot drink and carried it up to her mother's bedroom. Cynthia was in bed. Her face was moist with the remains of the cold cream, her hair pulled back into a turban. She did not possess a nightdress but wore instead a man's shirt, as she always had. She was lying against a bank of pillows, smoking, an ashtray resting on her lap. Judith sat on the bed beside her. The room smelt of stale perfume and tobacco.

'I'm going to spend the night,' Judith said, and her mother nodded, as if expecting this. They sat without speaking for a while and then Judith said: 'Would you really have done it?'

Again Cynthia nodded and said: 'Well, they say death is a release, don't they?' and she smiled slightly, in irony. 'I thought it out the night you telephoned from the hospital: when you said you wouldn't be a martyr to a genetic accident. That stuck in my mind, I don't know why. Then I thought, all right, I'll take him from you, look after him for you. It would solve the problem. But then I knew it was useless, it would be more of a reproach than if he was living in a home somewhere. And I realised what had to be done and that it was up to me to do it.'

There were ash stains on the sheets and Judith silently rubbed at them with her forefinger. Cynthia's face was in profile, harshly illuminated by the light from the bedside table.

'But I overrated myself. I thought it would be easy to

178

deceive you. I thought in that one thing I couldn't possibly fail. I was just deceiving myself, wasn't I? So maybe I couldn't have gone through with it after all. I've made a complete mess of it, one way and another.'

'We both have,' Judith said, and Cynthia glanced at her.

'Yes, I forgot for a moment,' she said, 'that you're a mother too.'

After this Cynthia slept for a while and Judith returned to the kitchen where she washed and dried the dishes and swept the floor. Outside, it had stopped raining and the wind had dropped. She found an eiderdown in a cupboard and wrapped it around herself and lay on a bed in an upstairs room. At dawn her mother came in and they continued talking, this time Cynthia seated on the bed next to Judith. At one point Judith said: 'We talk of him as if he's a monster. As if he has to be exterminated. But he's not.'

'You make that sound like an apology.'

'It isn't. I know I've nothing to apologise for. It just suits us to think of him that way. Yet when you told me what you intended doing, I had this absurd feeling that I should protect him. I can't explain why.'

'There are no explanations for these things.'

They cooked breakfast in the kitchen and talked again, sitting huddled in front of the oven for warmth.

'On my way here last night,' Judith said, 'I was trying to think why you wanted him. Trying to work it out in my mind.'

Cynthia waited without speaking.

'I thought, finally she'll have the kind of relationship she wants. It would be entirely on her terms. But I knew even that was more than I could give him. I'm sorry.'

'For thinking it, or failing him?'

Judith considered the question a moment before replying.

'I don't know. Perhaps you're right. Perhaps I do feel the need to apologise after all.'

Then later she said: 'I wanted him dead, but I knew I'd do nothing about it. I was happy to let others do it for me. That's always been the difference between us.'

'I've done nothing about it either, as it turns out.'

'But the thought was there.'

'It was there for you, too. It's there for everyone in such a situation, at least for an instant. I just didn't want to let it go. Living alone does that. There's no one to dissuade you out of these things.'

'Would you have listened if there had been?'

A smile flickered briefly across Cynthia's face. She looked almost youthful in the daylight; there was no trace of the years or the events of the previous night.

'Probably not,' she said.

* * *

They talked intermittently, only occasionally apprehensive of the other's silence. They wondered if they should go out, but were reluctant to face the world outside. They lit a fire in the sitting room and piled it with old newspapers and dead flowers.

'You get ideas, even when you live with someone,' Judith said. She was sitting cross-legged by the fire, her mother in an armchair behind her. 'I thought at one time you had cancer. I thought that's what your trips to the hospital were all about.'

Cynthia laughed at this, as Judith knew she would, and she found herself laughing with her. When Cynthia told her it was the menopause, they laughed again.

A little later Judith fell asleep in front of the fire and Cynthia busied herself in the kitchen. When Judith woke her mother was seated in the armchair once again, as if she had never left it.

'Patrick will be wondering about me. I should go home.'

'Yes.'

'He wants another child, did I tell you? We're to move house and start a family and live happily ever after. It probably will be that simple too.'

'Yes,' Cynthia said again.

'All the same,' Judith said, the embers from the fire sparkling in her eyes, her face still flushed with sleep, 'all the same, I think I'll stay a little longer.'

Chapter Twenty-Two

A week later Patrick called round. When the knock came on the door Judith found herself tensing; she knew instantly that it was Patrick. Cynthia let him in and led him to the kitchen. The room seemed crowded with the three of them inside it and after a moment Cynthia withdrew. In her presence Patrick's head had been lowered, shyly, but now he raised it, darting a quick look at Judith. He had an odd, nervous smile on his face.

'I've come to collect you,' he said.

'I told you, I'm staying a few days.'

'Let Cynthia stay with us, if it's company you need.'

'It isn't.'

'I see. I suppose then it's just my absence you prefer?'

'I simply want to stay with my mother for a few days, that's all.'

'Ah yes, of course. Your mother with whom you're so close. Forgive me, I'd overlooked that.'

His voice was strained, his eyes glittering and hard. He

was dressed in a suit for work, its creases sharp and immaculate. She felt grubby and unwashed before him.

'I need you at home,' he said.

'I'll be there in a day or two.'

'Why not now? There's nothing to keep you here you haven't already accomplished.'

'Patrick, don't make a scene, please.'

He seemed to respond to this appeal.

'No,' he said, 'of course not.'

He sat at the table, his fingers absently probing its rough surface.

'It's just that I've put the house on the market. I need you there to show people around.'

'Can't the estate agent do that? Just give them a key.'

'You should be there.' He said this simply and she did not contradict him.

'It's all coming along nicely. If we get a buyer as quickly as they say we should be able to exchange contracts inside a month.'

'Good. That's good.'

'But you haven't even seen the new house yet.'

'I'll trust your judgement. I always have, haven't I?'

'Oh, Judith.'

He turned his face away. She imagined his lips trembling. She could hear her mother coughing in the adjoining room. They were going to have shepherd's pie for lunch, and go for a walk in the afternoon. She did not want to carry the memory of Patrick's melancholy with her. She sat beside him and asked him questions about the house and watched his face light up as he talked about it. She told him then how their present home depressed her, how she felt more at ease in these familiar surroundings with Cynthia, with whom she was tentatively reconciled. He seemed surprised by this, but accepted it and waited, expecting her to ask him to stay with them, but she did not, and he seemed to accept this also, but with less surprise. Finally he said the change of scene was probably what they both needed. He would see to the selling of the house himself. When everything was signed and sealed they could move into their new home together. In the meantime he would visit or phone her every day. He seemed invigorated by the responsibility of his plans and this relieved her. When he left, he kissed her; he was breathing heavily, but he swiftly broke away from her and walked quickly to the front door, his head lowered once more.

She stood in the kitchen where he had left her, still feeling his breath on her cheeks. She knew he hadn't said half of what he intended to say, and this grieved her, as it clearly did him. She suddenly remembered her thoughts in the hospital bed about the baby and her inhibitions, and how the baby would liberate both Patrick and herself; she felt a sharp compassion for the child on whom so much had depended and then marvelled that she was now allowing herself to feel anything for him, even if it was only pity. It was true, he no longer threatened her as he once had. She still felt his presence, certainly, but it no longer filled her with unease. She had simply got used to it. It dawned on her that this was how it would be from now on. She would succumb to his presence, living somewhere apart from her, cared or uncared for, and she would absorb his presence within her where it would remain, implanted and inviolate; she would allow herself to dwell on him, as Cynthia had predicted, because it was her nature. It would be her punishment, but she would cope with it, because that was in her nature also.

A few moments later her thoughts returned to Patrick. She knew that when he came to consider it he would despise himself for his compliance with her decision not to return home with him that day, and, worse still, that he would eventually realise that she had engineered it.

✳   ✳   ✳

The pattern of Cynthia's days, although more solitary and self-absorbed, was largely unaltered from that of Judith's childhood and Judith found herself surrendering to it. The telephone did not ring with its old frequency, and Cynthia was more morose than she remembered, but otherwise the routine they shared was much as it had always been. The intimacy of the first few days was gradually replaced by an easy familiarity and then small flashes of antagonism which flared and died according to Cynthia's impulses; Judith surrendered to these also. Cynthia often disappeared from the house for hours at a time, vaguely saying on her return, and only when prompted, that she had been to an art gallery or to the cinema. She rarely asked Judith to accompany her.

One afternoon, while shopping, Judith caught sight of her mother in a café, talking with a young man, their heads bent together, their hands not quite meeting on the surface of the table between them. The sight of it depressed Judith. Her mother's face looked wrapt and vivacious, momentarily brought to life, as it always had been by the presence of a man. She hurried away from the café, but the memory of the expression on Cynthia's face did not leave her. She thought of it again that evening as they faced each other across the kitchen table over supper; the face she saw now was unrecognisable from the one she glimpsed in the café and it annoyed her that some nameless youth could evoke such a transition, whereas she could not. Later that evening she watched her mother sitting by the fire, restlessly flicking ash into the grate while half watching television and re-reading an old newspaper, and realised that Cynthia considered herself to be quite alone, and the thought diminished her,

Chapter Twenty-Two

as it had always done. Cynthia suddenly spoke: 'When do you expect Patrick next?'

'We spoke on the telephone this morning.'

'Next time you do ... ask him for some cash, will you?'

Judith frowned at this; the outline of her mother's face tautened slightly.

'It's only reasonable. He supports you at home, doesn't he?'

'Except I'm not at home, am I?'

'You still have to eat.'

'If you're short of money, Mother, why not say so?'

'I'm not. Not especially. But we could always do with some more. Besides, you're his wife.'

She said this simply, but imbued it with hidden implications. Judith thought of the monthly alimony cheques going into her mother's account.

'It's my choice not to live at home at the moment. Why should he have to pay for it?'

'Oh God, you're not going to get all proud about it, are you? I'm not talking about a handout. Just a few pounds here and there. He owes you that much.'

'Because of the baby?'

'No, no.' Cynthia's tone was impatient, as if Judith was deliberately prevaricating. 'But if nothing else I thought it might have taught you a little about self-pre-servation. You want to come out of the whole thing with nothing?'

'I haven't come out of anything. We're simply ... working things out until the new house is ready.'

'Then there's nothing to work out, is there? Every-thing's dandy.'

Cynthia gave a short, hard laugh and returned to her paper, but a second later lowered it. She looked oddly determined, as if she was reluctant to speak but in spite of herself compelled to do so.

'Your father was not unlike Patrick, you know. Good and gentle. But qualities like that become a trifle tedious if they're not sharpened by something else. Oh, you tell yourself they're important and worthwhile but each time the argument is a little less convincing. I know the signs, I went through it myself. I now allow your father to provide for me, because he's still got those qualities and if I'd stayed with him I would have drummed them out of him ... we both know that and we know the arrangement we now have is a fair exchange.'

'Or you've just convinced yourself into a convenient justification.'

This was barely more than a sullen murmur, and Cynthia disregarded it.

'Yes, well, if you're sensible you'll do the same thing.'

'The situation isn't the same and I'm not you, am I?'

'Perhaps not, but you're not as unlike me as you want to think.'

Judith felt herself flushing. She left the room and stood in the kitchen, rebuking herself for allowing the conversation to disturb her, and then unwillingly acknowledged why it had. She saw not only that the brief respite with her mother was nearing its end, but that when that end came she had not prepared herself for what lay after it. She was exhausted by the prospect of facing another decision and angry with her weakness for being so unable to confront it. At least in this one respect she knew herself to be different from her mother.

While Judith pondered these things in the kitchen, Cynthia sat waiting in the sitting room, straining for a sound of her daughter. She, too, was rebuking herself, not for her words but for their harshness. She had known Judith would resist her suggestion concerning Patrick, and had consciously used this, not to her own advantage, but hopefully to Judith's. It seemed that all her attempts to protect her daughter would have to be administered in this negative way, but she knew also that she was quite incapable of handling it differently. Judith's passivity always forced her into unlikeable extremes, she had long since recognised this. But to what extremes had she now propelled her daughter? She sat contemplating this for some moments, her eyes closed, wondering why she made such complexities out of such simple issues; for the desire to see her daughter happy was simple, it was just the means by which it could be accomplished which had become so intolerably complicated.

* * *

The next day Judith went with Patrick to see the new house. It was almost exactly as he had described it and as she had imagined: tall and spacious and untidy. The ghosts of the previous tenants seemed friendly and she immediately understood why it had appealed to Patrick. The walls were, for the most part, painted in primary colours. There was a wide central staircase with a window set in the roof at the top which illuminated both the stairwell and the hall in a soft, white light.

Patrick escorted her from room to room, explaining the function of each and his plans for renovation. Many of the rooms had been bedsitting rooms and still contained sinks and cookers. The upper storey (there were three in all) was a converted attic space and had sloping ceilings and small dormer windows enclosed in the steep slope of the roof. There was a solidity about the house which impressed Judith, and, despite herself, she felt something of her old enthusiasm returning. One room in particular caught her imagination. It was the largest on the top floor and painted lilac; the sloping beams of the ceiling thrusting sharply into the floor, so that the room seemed part of the support structure of the house itself. It was the room Patrick had designated as their bedroom.

At that moment she saw herself soothed and protected in this room and she stood quite motionless, feeling the presence of the room about her, and thought, Yes, after all, we could be happy in such surroundings, and then wondered why their happiness had always depended on a house or a room, and why it was so impossible to visualise it outside such a setting.

After seeing the house they went to a wine bar for lunch and talked about the house and what they would do with it. They talked intimately, but with a constraint which was rather formal. But these days, when she saw Patrick, Judith did not feel the old sense of anxiety. She felt almost friendly towards him, and he reciprocated in the same vein. They talked occasionally about the baby but more as a conversation point, a mutual experience, than through any sense of compulsion. They did not touch on Judith's reluctance to return home: the tension over this now lay dormant beneath their conversations, as something they knew to be beyond their articulation and understanding. They knew, also, that it was a finite state of affairs, and this became more obvious as their talk on the progress of the new house started to dominate their meetings. There was a definite momentum now to their encounters, and at the end of it stood the lilac room, like a centre of gravity where their lives could comfortably converge once more.

Chapter Twenty-Three

During this time Judith was sleeping badly. And when she opened her eyes in the morning she could still see the dislocated images of her dreams; even when she closed her eyes they refused to be exiled. She got up aching with exhaustion, physically spent by the emotions she had expended during the night. To her knowledge she did not dream of the baby, and she felt a little cheated by this; it seemed her unconscious was in league against her, preventing his expulsion from her conscious mind.

She dreamt frequently of Patrick, however, of his touch, of the feel of him inside her, of his face above her, bloated and intent; and the strength of those dreams disturbed her too. Such images of sexuality were unlike her, and she was surprised to find herself so susceptible to them. Sometimes, when waking after these dreams, she masturbated, and this too was new, but she felt complete impunity about it, regarding it as something she was doing to herself rather than for herself. It brought her relief, certainly, but also into sharp confrontation with the fact that she was alone. The acknowledgement of this was her new method of self-chastisement.

The date for moving into the new house had now been set, and one night, two weeks before the date, she woke sweating and trembling with what she took to be fear. She instinctively reached out for Patrick, but his absence did not increase her fear and she knew he was not the cause of it. Then she remembered that she had experienced the fear before, in her childhood, and that it was always connected with a sense of loss. She got out of bed and tiptoed across the hall to her mother's bedroom, went in, and remembered that she had done this as a child when she had woken up with this feeling. She stood beside her mother's bed, listening for the sound of her breathing, straining every nerve until she heard it, breathed out in relief and returned to her own room.

Back in bed, she felt her fear subside, but the physical effects of it remained; she was still trembling and alert, her senses refusing to obey the commands of her brain to rest. Eventually she persuaded herself to sleep and woke late in the morning to see Patrick and her mother standing at the foot of the bed looking down at her. For an instant she thought they too were a dream and she blinked her eyes, expecting to find them gone, but instead they approached her, one each side of the bed, circling it in a manner which was familiar and she remembered it was the same as the paediatrician's manner had been that day. She saw a look pass between them and then they smiled, but it was a smile she did not recognise.

'He's dead.' It was Patrick who spoke, his voice veiled in a relief which was almost like pain. 'The baby. He's dead.'

* * *

It transpired he had died during the night. A social worker had caught Patrick before he went to work and told him. It was as a result of his heart condition, she said, complications had set in, followed by pneumonia. Later that day Judith spoke to the social worker on the telephone and the funeral arrangements were decided upon. He was to be cremated the following day in Bournemouth, where he had been transferred to a nursery for handicapped babies. Patrick said that no one from the family should attend. Apart from anything else, he added, it would be hypocritical. It was a powerful argument and Judith conceded to it.

The telephone started to ring again. Patrick had spread the news and friends rang Cynthia's home with messages of condolence but uttered in tones more reminiscent of congratulation. Judith found herself shuddering in distaste, but it was directed at herself, for their obvious lack of grief exactly mirrored her own. She did not display her disgust, however, for the spectre of hypocrisy at that moment seemed equally, if not more, unpalatable than that of relief.

In the afternoon Patrick returned to the office and Judith returned to her bedroom, assuming that by confining herself in such a way her grief would have no choice but to emerge. But it did not. Realising this, she prepared to go downstairs once more. She combed her hair and looked at herself in the mirror and thought, So it's not over after all, how absurd to think it was. Even the idea of this did not dismay her; it simply confirmed something she felt she already knew.

Patrick stayed with her that night, but they did not make love. He simply held her and she rested against him, listening to the sound of the television in the sitting room beneath them, where Cynthia was watching a late night film. After a while Patrick said: 'There's this chap at the office, Wilson, a sombre sort of chap, but reliable, you know. When he heard the baby had died, he sought me out. I just wasn't in the mood. He's religious, and I just wasn't in the frame of mind for all that. It was all very strained and he started talking about the baby and I said, "What was the point? Such a short life, so much bloody misery for everyone. For what?"'

Judith lay quite still in his arms, listening. 'And he said, which was predictable, because he's that sort of fellow, that even butterflies have a point to their existence, have the right to live, even if it's only for a few days. That made me angry. I hate that kind of talk, as you know. I said to him, "But butterflies are beautiful so they bring that out in others, don't they? All our child did was bring out ugliness."'

'What did he say?'

'Oh, you can imagine. He said if there was a point maybe it was that.'

Judith considered this in silence a moment, then she said: 'Do you feel ugly because of it?'

Patrick hesitated before replying. She felt his arm stiffen under her.

'I was starting to, I think. And you?'

'I suppose I never considered myself to be anything else.'

He flashed a look at her, his expression bewildered.

'Don't say things like that.'

'Why? You think that by not saying it, it will be any the less true? Like everything else we don't discuss?'

He sighed at this, and turned his head away.

'We will, you'll see. It'll all be as it was before. Everyone has something to overcome in their lives, and this has been ours. And we're through it. It's downhill all the way from now on.'

A few moments later he was asleep.

*   *   *

The next morning Patrick rose early: he had to go home to change into clean clothes for the office. After he'd gone, Judith rang the social worker again, while Cynthia cooked breakfast in the kitchen. When Judith had finished on the telephone she joined her mother, who was standing at the cooker, a fork in her hand, frying bacon.

'I'm going out, Mother. I might be late, so don't wait up for me.'

Cynthia turned to look at her daughter and her eyes seemed almost amused.

'You're going to Bournemouth, aren't you?'

'Yes.'

'So Patrick didn't persuade you out of it?'

'No.'

Cynthia smiled, but the amusement in her eyes had given way to something else.

'I'll take you at your word then. I won't wait up for you.'

She turned back to the cooker and the business of the bacon. A few minutes later she heard the front door slam. She took the bacon off the gas and drained away the sizzling fat and then she switched on the radio and tuned into a discussion programme. She had become accustomed to the sound of voices in the house.

Chapter Twenty-Four

She took a taxi from the station to the crematorium, which was on the outskirts of Bournemouth. It was a squat, circular building, adorned with colonnades and several miniature sculpted porticos which led directly to the various chapels. The furnace itself was housed in the centre of the building, out of sight; the chapels were on varying scales of grandeur and size.

The service for John David was to be in one of the smaller, more modest ones, at the rear of the crematorium. It was an imposing, narrow room, with rows of wooden benches divided in the centre by an aisle, reminiscent of a church, but there was an impersonal austerity about the place which Judith had not anticipated. The walls were bare and at the far end was a raised plinth overhung by tassled, red velvet curtains, which were closed. It had the look of a puppet theatre about it. There were two other people present, seated at the front. Judith recognised the robust figure of the local authority social worker, sitting upright in her belted mackintosh, her eyes on the curtains. Next to her sat a young girl, aged around nineteen. Judith caught a glimpse of her profile, a slightly fleshy, waxen face and heavy, deep-set eyes. Her hair was tied back in an elastic band, her head was bowed. As Judith entered the social worker seemed to sense her presence, and turned to acknowledge her with a quick smile. The young girl also turned, her features strained, and Judith instantly knew she was one of the nurses who had cared for the baby in the nursery. There was no hint of reproach in the girl's face however; she simply inspected Judith with a kind of candid, detached interest, before turning away. Judith had never before felt so utterly dismissed.

A few moments later a priest entered. He was blond and young. He stood on a small dais to the right of the curtains and took some notes from his pocket, together with a prayer book. As he did this, the curtains glided soundlessly open and the coffin was revealed. Judith stared at it; a burning sensation crept upwards from her stomach, like a scald, embedding itself in her chest so that she found it difficult to breathe. The coffin was plain and unadorned and pathetically small. She thought of the baby's face as she had last seen it in the hospital, and she thought of him now, encased inside the casket, and the two images collided; she felt herself splintering under the impact. In that second she understood, as she had done once before, but had since refused to acknowledge, that she and the baby had been locked in a combat to survive, and that she had won. Only now that he was dead could she see her adversary for what he was, and always had been, weak and vulnerable, and that her victory over him was inevitable and quite without mercy. She saw that she had denied herself the chance to grieve for his condition, or to question her rejection of him. She could grieve now, not only for his death, but for the alien spirit he had woken within her, which had so crushingly extinguished him, and from which there was no retreat for her. She heard herself saying the word 'no' to the social workers, and she knew she would hear herself saying it again, for she now knew its power and its potential.

Outside the crematorium, the air was humid. She could hear the roar of the traffic and feel the jostle of people brushing past her. Briskly, she set off; there was an urgency to her steps, for she was anxious to reach her destination.

If you would like to know more about Virago books, write to us at Ely House, 37 Dover Street, London W1X 4HS for a full catalogue.

Please send a stamped addressed envelope

VIRAGO
Advisory Group

Andrea Adam   Zoë Fairbairns
Carol Adams   Carolyn Faulder
Sally Alexander   Germaine Greer
Anita Bennett   Jane Gregory
Liz Calder   Suzanne Lowry
Bea Campbell   Jean McCrindle
Angela Carter   Cathy Porter
Mary Chamberlain   Alison Rimmer
Anna Coote   Elaine Showalter (USA)
Jane Cousins   Spare Rib Collective
Jill Craigie   Mary Stott
Anna Davin   Rosalie Swedlin
Rosalind Delmar   Margaret Walters
Christine Downer (Australia)   Elizabeth Wilson
Barbara Wynn

Book Tokens

Give them the pleasure of choosing
Book Tokens can be bought and exchanged at most bookshops